Contents

Managing Change in Health and Social Care Services

Terry Scragg

Managing Change in Health and Social Care Services

Published by:
Pavilion Publishing (Brighton) Ltd
Richmond House
Richmond Road
Brighton
BN2 3RL
UK

Tel: 01273 623222
Fax: 01273 625526
Email: info@pavpub.com
Web: www.pavpub.com

First published 2010.

A catalogue record for this book is available from the British Library.

ISBN: 978-1-84196-282-5

Pavilion is the leading training and development provider and publisher in the health, social care and allied fields, providing a range of innovative training solutions underpinned by sound research and professional values. We aim to put our customers first, through excellent customer service and value.

Authors: Terry Scragg, with Janet McCray
Editor: Catherine Jones, Pavilion
Cover design and Page layout: Tony Pitt, Pavilion
Typesetting: Emma Garbutt, Pavilion
Printing: Aquatint

In memory of Dennis Marsden

Acknowledgements

This book is based on experience gained over many years of working in health and social care services, in practitioner, management and consultancy roles, and draws on a wide range of examples of organisational change. This experience has left me with a deep appreciation of the complexity of change and the dedicated work of managers and professionals who have taken responsibility for improving their services. One of the reasons for writing this book was to bring together the many themes and approaches to change that I have witnessed, or engaged with directly, in research and consultancy assignments across a wide range of health and social care services, and that I trust will be helpful to managers and professionals in the future.

In writing this book I would like to thank a number of people who have helped me at various stages of the production process. They have variously provided suggestions for chapters, case studies or have read earlier drafts. They include Taff Davies, Charlotte Dawber, Peter Gilbert, Simon Livesley, Debbie Medlock and Lucy Scragg. I would particularly like to thank Janet McCray for agreeing to write a chapter on change in inter-professional contexts, which is an increasingly important area of development in health and social care services. Throughout the writing stage I have had support from Sanaz Nazemi, Catherine Jones and Tony Pitt at Pavilion Publishing. Their editorial guidance, encouragement and support has been invaluable. Lastly, I would like to thank Susan for her continuing support throughout the preparation of this book.

Terry Scragg

About the authors

Terry Scragg is a visiting fellow at the University of Chichester where he formerly led postgraduate management programmes for health and social care managers. He has worked in the NHS and social services departments in practitioner and management roles, and has undertaken a wide range of research and consultancy throughout the UK, focusing on organisational change. He has held non-executive roles in two health authorities and is currently a charity trustee of a learning disability service in West Sussex.

Janet McCray is principal lecturer in health and social care leadership at the University of Chichester. Janet trained originally as a learning disability nurse and has had a wide range of practice and academic experience in health and social care services. She has undertaken and published research in the field of inter-professional and multi-professional learning, leadership and practice.

Foreword

Managing Change in Health and Social Care Services is written for the contemporary reader who lives in a world where the trinity of single source solutions, high quality specifications and accessibility, or ease of use, are fundamental. Terry Scragg distils and presents an extensive range of classic management theories and techniques, like the SWOT analysis and PESTEL analysis, the 7-S model and culture analysis. Up-to-date leadership theories are presented with references to integrity and values, which are essential to successful and sustainable change.

This handbook should be standard issue for all new managers in health and social care. The transition from clinician or practitioner to manager will be well supported by the aids to structured thinking contained within these pages – this is not an empty suggestion. In a previous organisation where I was responsible for management development we issued Terry's 2001 publication *Managing at the Front Line* to our frontline managers. I will similarly provide *Managing Change in Health and Social Care Services* as standard reference to colleagues and associates of HS Consultancy. Established managers and leaders will also benefit from this comprehensive handbook. It serves as a reminder that the same evidence-based and structured decision-making required in direct work with service users must also be modelled by those managing change in organisations.

Managers in health and social care are today more frequently required to implement large scale and radical changes. At the time of writing, the public sector in the UK is faced with the largest scale of change in a generation, while services are responding to unprecedented cuts in finances as a result of the global economic downturn. At the same time they are faced with service and system reconfigurations and changes in approach precipitated by new government policy. This new wave of change is set to last for several years and is likely to set a baseline of possibilities against which future change proposals will be assessed. Successful management through these challenges requires intellectual rigour as well as interpersonal competence and emotional intelligence. True to form, Terry ensures that with their adherence to the trinity of single source solutions, quality and accessibility, no manager required to deliver change can legitimately raise the claim 'no one told me how'. I invite managers in health and social care and beyond to read this book and then find a way to translate the learning into everyday management practice.

Hári Sewell
Director, HS Consultancy
Chair of the Social Care Strategic Network
July 2010

Introduction

Change is constant

Change is a constant in all our lives, whether it is making personal changes in our daily routines or responding to the impact of wider changes in society that offer new opportunities for growth and development. Evolution teaches us that organisms continually adapt to their environment in order to survive, and those that fail to adapt eventually perish. These theories have implications for all organisations which must continually adapt to their external environment and use processes of change to achieve success. When health and social care organisations fail to adapt to changes in their environment they eventually provide services that no longer fully meet the needs of those that use them, and although they may not perish, as species do in the natural world, they reach a stage where they stagnate or permanently fail.

Reasons for the book

Managers and professionals involved in implementing change, whether it is a strategic change initiative or operational adjustments to day-to-day practice, face many challenges. It is these challenges that can be helped by an understanding of the concepts and techniques of change management. This is particularly important when change is resisted, even when it is obvious that improvements are long overdue. An understanding of the individual responses to change can offer useful insights into the impact of change when it disturbs or threatens the routines and expectations of staff. A personal involvement in change projects over many years has revealed the difficulties managers and professionals can face, and why the lesson learned from this experience points to some essential elements in any change initiative that need to be understood if they are to increase the potential for successful implementation. By exploring the different stages of change, from initial ideas and proposals through to implementation and evaluation, this book is intended to support managers and professionals by describing the concepts of change, supported by numerous case examples of both successful and unsuccessful change initiatives.

The growing pace of change

Organisations providing health and social care services have changed continually since their inception in the post-war period. Although the basic purpose of these services has remained remarkably constant, for a long period change was incremental and did not disturb the organisational arrangements or professional practice significantly. This gradual change was based on the premise of predictability and continuing improvement, and a political consensus about the organisation of services. It was felt that with sufficient gradual improvement in services, through incremental change, they would keep in step with their external environment and its demands.

These assumptions were shattered with the organisational transformations as part of the public sector reforms of the early 1990s and the introduction of markets in health and social care. These changes brought with them management ideas and concepts from the private sector, radically different from the earlier traditional model of public administration. These market-based reforms fundamentally changed the structure of services, and separated the purchasers and providers, increasingly involving the private and voluntary sector in the provision of services. The election of a Labour government in 1997 did nothing to reduce the pace of change, continuing the previous Conservative policies and ushering in a period of further reform with the policy of modernisation that continues to the present day, although in a changing political and financial climate.

The last decade has seen an unprecedented level of change in health and social care services, with the intention of improving performance and making them more accessible and sensitive to the needs of people using them. These changes have meant the development of new or restructured organisations, and roles and styles of working, as services move beyond traditional service delivery to more subtle approaches that recognise the influence of a range of different agencies, partnerships and user perspectives. What is different about this most recent period of change is the pace and scope of what is being expected of services, and the need for those leading services to develop a more sophisticated understanding of the management of change.

This book does not start from the presumption that all change is good. A significant amount of recent change that has taken place in public services has been damaging and costly to services and has often demoralised managers, professionals and support staff. Much of this has stemmed from a lack of appreciation of the complexity of health and social care services and the difficulty of implementing change without the commitment and understanding of those who have to carry out new roles and practices. Change can also have other negative consequences which need to be recognised. It diverts time and effort from the ongoing challenge of improving services and the impact at the front line can be minimal. A serious side effect of continuous change is that it undermines a service's potential to respond to the needs of its service users, as individuals become preoccupied with internal structures and processes that ignore the world beyond the boundaries of the organisation. It is testament to the commitment of staff in health and social care services that they strive to maintain the quality of services in spite of the pressures of change.

Understanding the need for change

This book does not argue that there should be no change, rather that change is essential in both health and social care services in order to continually improve the quality of treatment and care provided, but also to respond to the longer-term demands of higher expectations and a growing older population with greater health and social care needs. Another urgent reason why change is essential is in response to the current financial crisis and reduced funding for public sector organisations that will threaten all services for years to come. This points to the importance of innovation, if new and more radical ways of organising and delivering services are to be developed in the future. As we move into an era of severe financial constraints on public services, making changes that improve efficiency and thereby reduce costs, alongside increases in effectiveness that deliver better services for users, will become ever more important. At a time when individuals working in health and social care services feel vulnerable and exposed to powerful economic forces beyond their control, the skilful and sensitive management of change will become ever more important.

Chapter synopsis

The first four chapters of this book cover a wide range of organisational issues, starting in Chapter 1 with an exploration of the forces that drive change, particularly in the external environment, and the importance of understanding these forces through the use of analytic tools and techniques. Chapter 2 describes the different factors that lead to the need for strategic and operational change and some of the pressures on public sector organisations when change is forced on them or corporate change programmes are introduced. Chapter 3 describes the importance of the context for change, drawing on a series of research studies, which highlight the importance of understanding those factors that influence receptivity to change. Chapter 4 introduces the power of organisational culture, and how deeply held beliefs and assumptions about organisations can make change difficult to achieve.

The next four chapters focus on the individuals who are central to change. Chapter 5 is concerned with leadership and the qualities needed by those leading organisations if they are to create a convincing vision for change, and support individuals and teams through the demands of implementation. Chapter 6 explores how responses to change are dependent to a great extent on the way that change is introduced and managed. The effective management of the change demands an understanding of the processes that need to be put in place to ensure that individuals are motivated by the prospects of improvement and supported as they take on new ways of working. Chapter 7 is concerned with the techniques of managing change and the range of tasks and techniques that can support managers when they are planning implementation. It is one thing to have a convincing strategy for change, but another to see that strategy translated into new structures, systems and processes, particularly at the front line. Chapter 8 explores the concept of stakeholding and the power and influence of stakeholders who have the potential to support or undermine the best designed change strategies. An understanding of how stakeholders view particular change proposals is crucial for successful implementation.

The final three chapters examine issues of managing change in inter-professional services, the importance of innovation in services, a summary of the book and some useful resources for further study. Chapter 9 explores the complex nature of inter-professional collaboration, with examples from service delivery, and the leadership action necessary to support changes in practice. Chapter 10 describes how innovation differs from routine change, and the enablers and conditions needed to ensure that organisations continue to innovate and introduce new ideas. In Chapter 11 there is a summary of the chapters and the final chapter has suggestions for further reading, including books, websites and web publications.

How you can use this book

How you decide to use this book will very much depend on your needs. It is first and foremost a practical resource to support you and is not intended to be read from cover to cover. It is a book to dip into when you need to understand some aspect of the change process, from a preliminary assessment of the need for change, through to implementation and evaluation. The intention is that it will help you improve your understanding of the different stages of the change process by focusing on some of the key stages where important decisions have to be made. It should be stressed that a handbook of this nature cannot possibly cover all aspects of managing change and some important aspects of the change process have been dealt with superficially. Should you wish to explore a particular aspect of change in more depth, each chapter has references that can be followed up, and the final section lists a number of useful books and websites that provide additional information on the management of change.

Section 1:

Organisational issues

Chapter 1

Analysing the need for change

Key points

- Importance of the vision and mission when considering change
- Analysis of the external and internal environment and what is driving change
- Analysing the need for change using PESTEL, 7-S and SWOT
- Using an optional appraisal to identify how to respond to change
- Value of widening participation when proposing change

Introduction

When planning change, particularly of a strategic nature, it is important that it only takes place after a thorough analysis of the factors driving the change and the possible costs and benefits to the organisation. Change should be approached with caution as it is all too easy for teams planning change to lack a full understanding of its impact on the organisation due to inadequate analysis of the internal and external environment. This is not to argue that change should never take place, in fact a well managed organisation will be making continual incremental adjustments as the need arises, and more radical change when conditions in its internal, or external, environment demand it. This chapter will explore how the analysis of environmental drivers can provide a sound basis for change.

Strategic analysis

A strategic analysis is a recognition of the need for change as a result of declining performance or new developments or threats to an organisation. These pressures require an understanding of the organisation's internal environment and its strengths and weaknesses, and the external environment and its opportunities and threats. What follows is a series of stages that planning teams can use to ensure that they thoroughly analyse the factors impacting on the organisation, both internally and externally. Each stage uses tools or processes that can help you make sense of the information collected and provide the basis for a more considered approach to change options.

Stage 1: Vision and mission

No matter where you start on the planning process, in the end you will need to go back to the vision and mission of the organisation as you are unlikely to be successful in planning change if you are not clear about where the organisation is headed. The vision should emphasise the purpose, performance and standards of the organisation, and serve the public rather than the organisation. Bryson (2004) argues that organisations should have a vision statement which:

- clarifies the organisation's direction and purpose
- is relatively future oriented
- reflects high ideals and challenging ambitions
- captures the organisation's uniqueness and distinctive competences, as well as desirable features of its history, culture and values
- is concise and inspiring
- is widely circulated, internally and externally
- is used to inform organisational decisions.

Bryson believes that the value of a vision statement, which is widely used in an organisation, is that it provides an idea of what success and desirable behaviour look like and, particularly, where clear guidance and decision-making can be derived from. It makes it easier for staff to discriminate between preferred and undesirable actions and outcomes that as a consequence produce more of what is preferred. A vision of success is important in helping an organisation to stay in touch with its environment and enables it to respond positively to crises – which confront all organisations during times of rapid change – as it promotes the learning and adaptation necessary to avoid crisis and threat.

The mission statement and its purpose

According to Courtney (2002), a mission statement helps to describe the boundaries of an organisation and its activities. It helps motivate staff and creates a sense of unity and focus for all stakeholders. It can also help in the process of evaluation of the organisation. Drucker (1990) sees the mission statement rooted in three main factors:

- the things the organisation does well – its strengths or core competencies
- where it is able to make a significant contribution to meeting needs
- what the people who work in the organisation really believe and are committed to.

Re-examining the mission is particularly important as it enables different members of the change team to discuss their views and reach consensus on the future direction. This stage is valuable in itself as it provides the motivation and guidance for the following stages of the process. The key questions are: what are we here to achieve (the purpose)? And what does the organisation need to do to achieve its purpose (the main aims)?

Descriptions of vision and re-examination of the mission can be helpful to provide direction for the subsequent stages of analysis. Realistically, teams may not start at this stage of analysis as often they may have to respond to threats that demand an immediate response, or if some aspect of strategy needs implementation then these actions will not wait on analysis. It is not uncommon for the subsequent stages of analysis to be completed first, with teams returning to their work on the vision and mission once strategic issues become clearer. Bryson (2004) has described the process as iterative, flexible and action-oriented, which can avoid participants feeling frustrated when they find they cannot complete the process sequentially. Bryson describes planning teams continuously rethinking the connections between the different elements in the process on the way to formulating the changes necessary to achieve the new strategy.

Stage 2: Understanding the external environment

What are the key drivers for change?

The next stage in the process is to examine both the current and future environmental influences for change as the future impact of environmental factors on an organisation may be different from those that influenced it in the past. Looking at where these changes come from will identify a series of key drivers that will help you understand the reasons why change may be necessary. The PESTEL framework is useful here as it will help identify a range of drivers that can impact on an organisation (see Figure 1.1 on p.15). PESTEL stands for political, economic, social, technological, environmental and legal.

Different elements of the PESTEL framework may also be more important to some organisations than others. For example, the political, economic and social factors are major influences on the social care services, whereas the NHS also has to consider the impact of technology, particularly in the acute sector (Upton & Brooks, 1995).

Factors that influence change can interact with each other and although there may appear to be a main driver, for example, a politically driven change will likely emerge from changes in social factors that politicians have to respond to, in reality few will stand alone as the sole driver. It is also important to recognise that change always takes place within a context and that contextual factors will significantly influence the scope and potential for change (see Chapter 3).

Political influences

The political influences cover a range of factors including legislation, governmental policies and the relationship between government and organisations, particularly public sector organisations. Politically driven changes are a major source of influence on health and social care services and have historically had the greatest impact on them, with the level of politically driven change having increased rapidly over the last two decades. Legislation and government policy initiatives influence the organisational structures, professional practice and distribution and quality of services, and these services are highly politicised as a result.

Economic influences

The economic factors that influence services include government funding of health and social care services, consumer expenditure and disposable income, labour costs, unemployment and recruitment. Health and social care services are public sector organisations whose main source of funding is controlled by government. As a consequence, the amount of money governments are willing to spend on health and social care directly impacts on these services and what they can achieve. A combination of political and economic influences can be seen in the policies of Conservative governments of the 1980s and 1990s, which were concerned to reduce the size of the state and the cost of public services, and passed legislation to achieve this policy objective. This led to the introduction of markets in health and social care with the intention of driving down costs, among other objectives, through the introduction of business methods.

Social influences

The social influences include demographic trends, shifts in values and culture, lifestyle changes, and expectations of service users. One of the most important social influences on health and social care services is the change in the demographic structure of society, with rapidly increasing life expectancy resulting in older people constituting a greater proportion of the population. As people age they increasingly need support from a range of services to help them retain their independence, particularly for those living alone or who have poor support networks. These changes will also affect health care as older people make greater demands on these services. As older people express a preference for support in their own homes, pressures on community based services will increase.

Technological influences

Technological influences include government spending on research and development, adoption of new technology, and new discoveries and products. The growth in assistive and enabling technologies are examples of recent developments in the health and social care fields that are providing support to enable people with disabilities or older people to improve the quality of their lives. Technological change has been so pervasive, particularly in the area of information technology, in that it has radically changed society within a generation. This has in turn had a major impact on health and social care services. The rate of technological change in both health and social care is seen in the potential to improve communications, provide greater access to information, both for professionals and users of services, and the potential to spread best practice through rapid communication.

Environmental

Environmental influences include environmental protection laws, energy consumption and waste disposal. This is a more recent driver for change, but one that is becoming increasingly important as threats to the environment through the use of energy, carbon emissions, and the long-term impact of pollution are recognised. The threat of climate change is now driving political and economic decisions to a greater extent than ever before and is likely to have adverse effects on health in the future. The environment has consequences, in health and social care, both in terms of the need to design systems and processes that minimise their impact on the environment and in longer-term strategies necessary to respond to the climate change agenda. For example, all health and social care organisations are now required to develop policies and practices that are more sustainable through an improvement in recycling of materials and waste, particularly controlled and hazardous waste. Further initiatives include carbon reduction schemes that cover all public sector organisations.

Legal

These factors include legislation, government and European directives, decisions of regulators and the courts. Health and social care services are subject to a wide range of government and European directives. The growth of health and safety procedures influences all aspects of operations in health and social care services. There have been directives from the European Parliament, for example, the Working Time Directive, which has had a significant impact on the working hours of NHS junior doctors and resulted in substantial change in working arrangements for junior medical staff. Alongside legislation and directives, separate from government, there are the powers of regulators, such as the Quality Care Commission (CQC), which is responsible for the regulation and inspection of health and social care services. For example, the CQC can order the closure of a care facility if it fails to meet the standards set out in the Care Standards Act (2000) and finds a facility's standards are poor or practice is unsafe following an inspection. It can also fine or order NHS trusts to close facilities where they fail to meet minimum standards.

Analysis of the external environment

Although the PESTEL technique is useful in asking key questions about the forces at work in the environment of a service, it is of limited value if it remains merely a list of influences. In using PESTEL it is necessary to go beyond the simple listing of factors and analyse the potential impact of each factor and its implications for a particular service. One way of using it is described by Smith (1994), as follows:

- take each of the six elements in turn
- identify possible trends that could affect your organisation
- seek to establish the most likely trend or the range of the most likely trends
- think through what the impact on your service would be if you were to continue into the future with your present strategies.

It is also important to ensure that the information in each PESTEL category is completed with reference to the aims of the service and the need for change so the exercise can move beyond simply listing factors (Iles & Sutherland, 2001).

Figure 1.1: PESTEL analysis

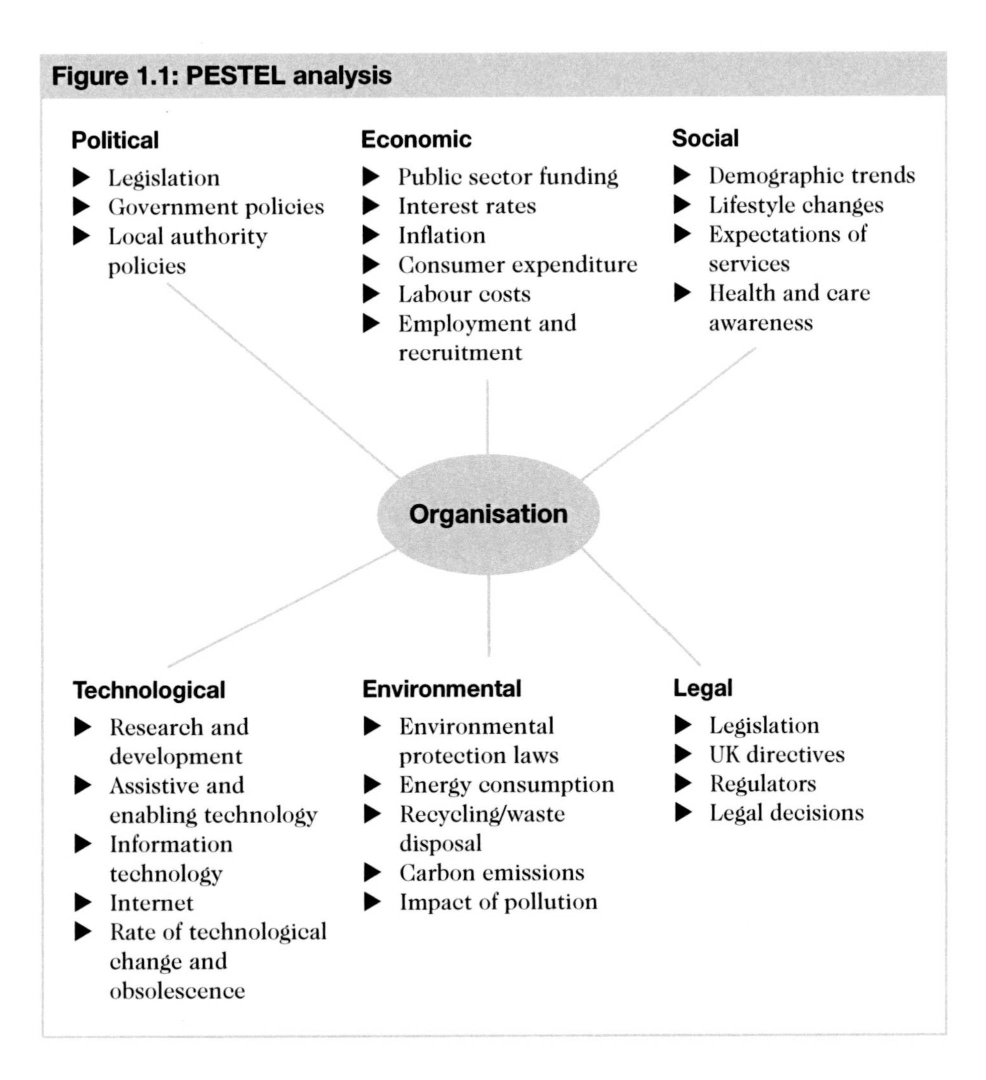

Auditing the change drivers

To take the analysis a stage further you could use an idea from Ross and Segal (2002) and identify each of the external drivers that you need to address and give them a score on a 1–10 scale, using the scale to rate each driver in terms of its importance to your service. This will enable you to identify those drivers that have the greatest potential impact (10), those that are of medium impact (5) and those which have low impact (1). It is likely that if you have a high score – lots of 10s – this suggests that your organisation is in a rapidly changing environment that requires an equally rapid response, whereas a low score might suggest that the organisation is operating in a stable environment, or you are just unaware of the risks approaching!

Stage 3: Analysis of the internal environment

The 7-S model

Once you have completed an external environmental assessment you next need to undertake an internal assessment. This will provide you with information on your organisation's internal effectiveness and its ability to respond to demands in the external environment. A starting point for an analysis of the internal environment of the organisation is Peters and Waterman's (1995) 7-S model for analysing an organisation's capability for change (see Figure 1.2 on p.18).

The 7-S model was developed to enable managers to understand that an effective organisation needs to attend to seven variables: strategy, structure, systems, staff, shared values, management style and skills. The authors argue that real change in organisations means attending to all seven areas of complexity. Taking each element in turn will alert you to how effectively your organisation performs. Use a series of questions, suggested by Iles (1997), to analyse your resources and competences.

- Strategy: what are you planning to do in response to, or in anticipation of, changes in the external environment, the needs of users and the strategies of competitors? You need to list all the services you provide and those who use them, and identify what your service does to meet users' needs, and how it is different from similar services. Do you know what users think about the service and those who fund it? What are they looking for from your service?
- Structure: describes the division of work among members of the organisation and how they are integrated and co-ordinated so they achieve the goals and objectives of the organisation. Structure is concerned with tasks and responsibilities, work roles and relationships, and channels of communication. The size and complexity of the organisation will dictate the need for structure. Small organisations can rely on personal and informal relationships, whereas larger organisations need formal structures to ensure that the activities of the organisation are planned, directed and controlled. When planning strategic change it is important to review the structure to ensure that it is in keeping with strategic developments.
- Systems: this describes the procedures, both formal and informal, that make the organisation 'work'. The list of systems in any health and social care organisation can be long and complex, and any changes need to be carefully designed to ensure that any new or modified processes are advantageous to the organisation. List the systems that are critical to the achievement of your strategy. What systems need to be in place to be able to deliver the strategy?

- Staff: do you have sufficient staff in the organisation with the correct skills who will actively support the strategy? Are they motivated to work energetically in support of the organisation's strategy?
- Skills: what skills are needed in the service? Do you have people with the right skills to support the strategy? If so, are they in the right place in the structure and supported by the right systems?
- Style: this describes the management style of senior staff and how they are seen by other members of the organisation. How are they viewed? What do they appear to value? And what is it that they do (as opposed to what they say)? What do they reward? These characteristics will determine the organisation's style.
- Shared values: this describes the culture of the service and the beliefs of staff and how this influences their behaviour. Beliefs are the shared norms that influence how users are treated, relationships with colleagues, managers and others, and views about the services and its future. Where beliefs are damaging to a service then they need to receive attention in order to correct them (see Chapter 4 for further discussion on culture).

Another factor to consider when using the 7-S model is that the elements that make up the framework can be considered as 'hard' and 'soft'. For example:

Hard elements	**Soft elements**
Strategy	Shared values
Structure	Skills
Systems	Staff

The hard elements are easier to identify as they are more under the control of management, whereas the soft elements are more difficult to manage as they are less tangible and more influenced by culture. Both are equally important if organisational change is to be successful.

Figure 1.2: The 7-S framework

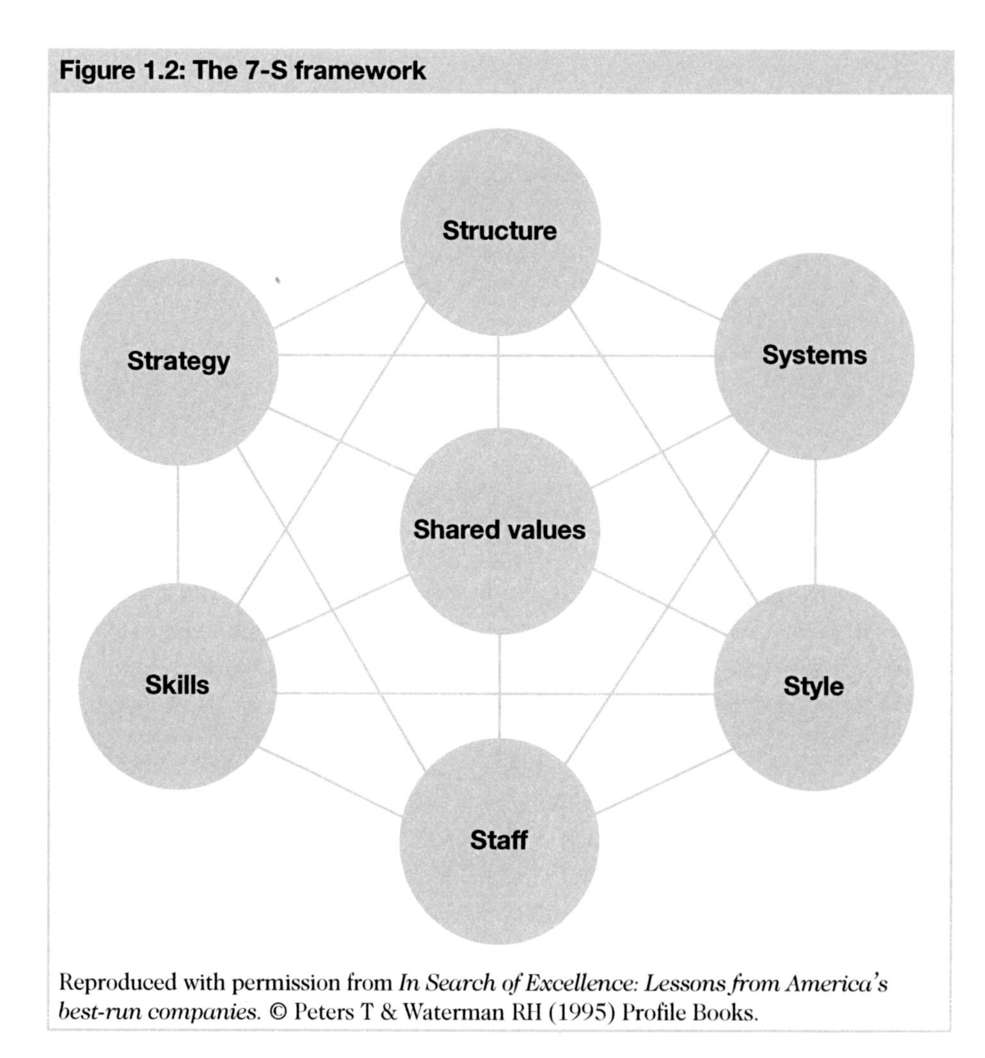

Reproduced with permission from *In Search of Excellence: Lessons from America's best-run companies.* © Peters T & Waterman RH (1995) Profile Books.

The value of considering the internal environment using the 7-S framework is the spotlight it throws on those parts of the organisation that work and are in harmony, and those that do not function effectively or are dissonant. Iles (1997) raises important questions for the manager about the organisation.

- Does the system support your strategy, and does it motivate staff and support them to develop and maintain the right skills?
- Does the structure take account of people in the organisation?
- Do the systems of communication support the structure?
- Is the style appropriate for the staff and for the strategy?
- Does everyone support the strategy?

Implications for the 7-S framework

Iles (1997) cautions that where the changes proposed affect one or more of the elements in the 7-S framework, you need to consider what impact this will have in turn on other elements. Any significant change will inevitably result in new or modified systems, and consequently working practices and skills, with possible changes in job descriptions and perhaps remuneration. Major change could also mean new attitudes are necessary, with changes to the culture of the organisation. In most organisations it is not the structure, system or individuals that are right or wrong or strong or weak in their own right, but only in relation to the other S elements in the framework. Iles makes the point that structure is only one of the seven elements that must support each other, but from the amount of restructuring in health and social care services one could be led to think this is the most important element.

Stage 4: SWOT analysis

The next stage of the analysis is the use of the SWOT (strengths, weaknesses, opportunities and threats) tool, which is a well known planning tool for identifying the external threats and opportunities facing an organisation, and the internal strengths and weaknesses of the organisation. Using the SWOT tool (see Figure 1.3 below) will ideally enable you to identify a change strategy that builds on the organisation's strengths, minimises its weaknesses, can overcome threats and takes advantage of opportunities. SWOT is easy to use, quick and productive, and that is its danger. As it is a straightforward checklist approach, simply listing factors has limited value. The importance is in the analysis, which needs to be as precise as possible, and how strategic decisions are informed as a result of the analysis.

Figure 1.3: SWOT analysis tool

Internal	
Strengths	Weaknesses
Opportunities	Threats
External	

A further danger of SWOT is restricting the analysis to a senior management team who, for a number of reasons, may not be in the best position to identify those factors most relevant to the organisation. Smith (1994) identifies three factors that can result from too narrow a perspective.

1. Members of the senior team planning change may not be well informed about the problems at the front line of the service, but which are critical for effective service delivery.
2. There may be an implicit attempt to justify the current strategies being pursued as these have resulted in earlier decisions by the senior team.
3. The analysis is not 'owned' by the wider staff group.

It is not practical, particularly in a large organisation, to consult all members of staff on the proposed changes, and this is where Smith recommends that focus groups can play a valuable role. The outcomes from focus groups and the management team leading the change can be compared, giving opportunities to consider a wider range of issues or differences in perception. The basic approach is to use brainstorming where a large number of ideas are generated, which at a later stage can be grouped under higher level headings leading to the identification of critical issues that the organisation needs to address and build on what the organisation does well.

As opportunities and threats are often difficult to identify, it is sensible to start the list with external environmental factors, before moving on to the internal strengths and weaknesses, which tend to be more familiar to most staff. A different approach is to create four groups and ask each group to take one of the headings in turn and then pass to another group to add additional factors, if they recognise them.

Opportunities

These arise from changes in the external environment, such as government policies or legislation that offer opportunities to provide new services. It could include changes in practice or changes in technology that the organisation can capitalise on due to its expertise. There could be new market opportunities due to changes in user need, or the withdrawal of competitors from the market. Opportunities could also arise from decisions to grow current services or develop new facilities. Importantly, do not assume that the external environment is static, rather that it is dynamic and can change rapidly.

Threats

These include external changes or developments that present risks to the organisation, such as reduced local authority funding, changes in legislation or policies that undermine existing services, and the entrance into the market of competitors with lower costs. A current change that is impacting on social care services is the decision of users with personal budgets to stop using some services, although this can present opportunities to an organisation through individuals purchasing less costly services.

Strengths

These are those aspects of the organisation including its market position, a high level of expertise, its physical and financial resources, highly motivated and committed staff, strong stakeholder involvement, its image and reputation. By identifying opportunities in the external environment that match the internal capabilities, the organisation can capitalise on its strengths.

Weaknesses

These are the deficiencies in the competences or resources of the organisation, such as a poor image or reputation, badly organised services or poor relationships with key stakeholders. A major task for managers is to work to correct those weaknesses that damage the organisation and reduce its effectiveness.

Stage 5: Strategic issues

Once the analysis has been completed, the SWOT findings are considered in relation to the strategic issues facing the organisation. Strategic issues are those that fundamentally affect the policies of the organisation, for example, in terms of its mission and values, the services it provides, the people who use the service and the financial health and effectiveness of its management. To complete this stage means considering each of the opportunities, threats, strengths and weaknesses in turn, and relating them to the vision and mission for the organisation.

Particular attention should be paid to clarity about what the issues are and how they are likely to impact on the organisation, rather than immediately seeking solutions. This can help avoid the risk of conflicts over solutions, rather than a thorough analysis of each issue and its implications for the organisation.

Bryson (2004) argues that the identification of issues generates a creative tension that is essential to stimulate organisational change. He suggests that organisations rarely change unless there is a felt need for change and that the issues that arise from an analysis of internal and external factors, particularly where they involve organisational survival or effectiveness, can provide sufficient tension to focus the attention of senior managers on the need for change. He identifies a series of useful questions that need to be answered.

- What is the issue?
- Why is it an issue?
- Who says it is an issue?
- What factors (mission, external and internal influences) make it a strategic issue?
- What are the consequences of failing to address the issue?
- Can we do something about it?
- What issues are missing from our analysis that our culture might have kept us from recognising?

The results of the discussion of these questions should be an identification and agreement about the critical issues facing the organisation that challenge its viability and success. Organisational change, particularly of a strategic nature, is often seen as too difficult or disruptive to address, and to overcome the inertia common in all organisations, requires strong leadership and commitment to deal effectively with the challenges faced. This stage should lead to a creation of a set of objectives that you want the change programme to achieve. These should be as specific as possible so that no ambiguity exists about what is proposed and it is clear what needs to change.

Stage 6: Option appraisal

Once the critical issues have been identified and a series of change objectives agreed, an appraisal of each objective in terms of how it could be met with different options can be explored. Depending on the urgency of the situation, some issues will need to be resolved immediately, particularly where these threaten the viability of the organisation, and will be of the highest priority. For other less urgent issues these can be explored at greater length to identify which is the best way to meet the objectives identified.

The following example from a learning disability service shows how the option appraisal can be used to identify the need for change in a service.

Threat: increasing numbers of users are choosing not to attend a current day service and brokers are not recommending it to users, with local authorities increasingly reluctant to fund the service.

Objective: provide day opportunities that are attractive to users, brokers and commissioners.

The options are:

1. investigate the reason users, brokers and local authorities no longer choose the service
2. based on feedback from a range of stakeholders, explore radically re-developing the service to make it more attractive, providing more flexible individualised activities to meet a range of users' needs
3. promote re-developed service with users, brokers and commissioners.

Who should be involved in analysing the need for change?

Although the responsibility for leading change rests with senior managers, who have specific responsibilities for the strategic development of an organisation, it is important to widen participation as much as possible. Senior managers can have a particular perspective based on their role and position in the organisation. Their view of the future could be dangerously narrow and they may interpret it as they would like it to be, or as they have always assumed it to be. They may also wish to justify the strategies that are already being pursued by the organisation. Senior managers also need to take into account their responsibilities under the Information and Consultation of Employees Regulations (Department of Business, Innovation and Skills, 2004), which affect all organisations with over 50 employees, and require employers to inform staff and consult with them when major changes are planned that may affect the workforce.

Involving other staff has considerable benefits as they will have a different perspective arising from their position in the organisation and their professional roles. You may not be able to involve all staff in each stage of developing a new strategy, but can involve them in designing and testing the robustness of a new strategy. This is important in developing ownership of change rather than seeing it as something that is imposed from the top without consultation. It can also play a valuable role in helping staff to understand the way the external environment is changing, which can have implications for their role and the service.

Where staff question the need for change, presenting them with the factors identified in the PESTEL and SWOT analyses can provide a wider perspective on the need for change. This can help dispel assumptions that change is the whim of senior management. It can show how the wider environment influences a service and cannot be ignored, and has to be addressed for the future health of the organisation. Non-executive members and trustees can also play an important part here as they bring a wider perspective to the strategic analysis and may have a more detached viewpoint on the possible implications of the trends revealed in a PESTEL and SWOT analysis.

Summary

In this chapter we have seen that change is a constant feature of all health and social care services and is influenced by a wide range of factors, particularly in the external environment. To understand how these changes can impact on an organisation there is a range of analytical tools available to managers embarking on change, including PESTEL, SWOT and the 7-S framework. All are invaluable for analysing change drivers and implications for systems and processes. Once the analyses are completed, the identification of key issues and options for change can help in identifying clear objectives for the change team. A further valuable purpose of these analytical tools is their potential to generate different perspectives on the need for change, and in doing so test the soundness of the proposed change, but also share information with staff in helping to explain why change is necessary.

References

Bryson JM (2004) *Strategic Planning for Public and Nonprofit Organizations: A guide to strengthening and sustaining organizational achievement*. San Francisco: Jossey-Bass.

Courtney R (2002) *Strategic Management for Voluntary Nonprofit Organizations*. London: Routledge.

Department of Business, Innovation and Skills (2004) *The Information and Consultation of Employees Regulations 2004* [online]. Available at http://www.opsi.gov.uk/si/si2004/20043426.htm (accessed June 2010).

Drucker P (1990) *Managing the Nonprofit Organization: Principles and practices*. New York: Harper Business.

Iles V (1997) *Really Managing Health Care*. Buckingham: Open University Press.

Iles V & Sutherland K (2001) *Organisational Change: A review for healthcare managers, professionals and researchers* [online]. London: NCCSDO. Available at http://www.sdo.nihr.ac.uk/files/adhoc/change-management-reviewpdf (accessed June 2010).

Peters T & Waterman RH (1995) *In Search of Excellence: Lessons from America's best-run companies*. London: Profile Books.

Ross B & Segal C (2002) *Breakthrough Thinking for Nonprofit Organizations*. San Francisco: Jossey-Bass.

Smith RJ (1994) *Strategic Management and Planning in the Public Sector*. Harlow: Longman.

Upton T & Brooks B (1995) *Managing Change in the NHS*. Buckingham: Open University Press.

Chapter 2

Strategic and operational change

Key points

- Change can take different forms depending on the pressures on an organisation
- Strategic change can be planned or forced, ranging from incremental to transformational change, dependent on the degree of strategic drift
- Changes can also be imposed on organisations by government
- Corporate change programmes can have their limitations
- Operational change is the continuous improvement at the front line of services
- A shared commitment and convergence of views about change and the value of organisational learning are important

Introduction

In this chapter we will explore the different forms that change can take and why some forms are more difficult to introduce successfully than others. The management of change is characterised by a wide range of activities that encompass both the strategic change, where managers incrementally tune and adapt the organisation to demands in its environment, or fundamentally transforms it, both in terms of structure and processes in the face of powerful pressures on the organisation. There is also the day-to-day operational change that takes place, usually continuously, in order to maintain or improve performance at the front line. Although incremental change has many advantages, there is also the risk of strategic drift and the consequences for organisations of ignoring changes in the external environment. Health and social care organisations can also have change forced on them by government and external agencies, or adopt change programmes that offer a 'magic bullet' to solving intractable problems, but can often disappoint in their impact.

Change takes different forms

Change can take many forms depending on a number of factors, including the focus of the change – will it affect the whole organisation, a particular part of the service or system, or individual roles? Will the change be planned, primarily by senior managers, or will it be emergent, with an adaptation to practices and processes on new ideas and information, or solutions to problems that have their origins in frontline operations? Will the change build on current ways of working with the assumption that more radical change is unnecessary, or will it be transformational, where it is recognised that fundamental change is necessary for the organisation to survive?

Strategic change

Strategic change can be described as all those activities that senior managers undertake to shape and guide the long-term development of an organisation in order to meet the demands of a changing environment and the expectations of stakeholders (Collier *et al*, 2001). In setting out the strategic direction for the organisation, senior managers will be concerned with matching the resources and activities of the organisation to its external environment in order to achieve a strategic fit. These activities may in turn involve change to structures, processes, roles and relationships.

Any change proposal, particularly of a strategic nature, is bound to change the organisation significantly in some way, and with it the relations between different groups and individuals, and is likely to encounter resistance in some form. Organisations where there has been a long period of continuity and energy placed on maintaining current activities have been described by Pugh (1993) as being 'ultra stable'. This can make implementation difficult as there is a tendency towards inertia and resistance to change in these organisations as people hold on to established ways of doing things and where change threatens existing beliefs about the purpose of the organisation. When change does take place it is often much too late with little time to consider alternatives, with the conflict and dislocation that follows as the organisation strives to cope with emergencies in order to survive.

Strategic change can also be difficult to manage in health and social care services as they operate in a political environment, which is relatively short-term in nature and turbulent and unpredictable at times (Alford, 2001). Alford describes managers of these services as subject to a diverse array of stakeholders who each place demands on organisations, with tensions between mandates from elected politicians that are at odds with the needs and wishes of other stakeholders, and who in turn overturn that mandate. This is most evident in policies to centralise services that face local opposition. Alford sees strategic change in public services as more open-ended and less subject to managerial control than in the corporate sector. It also makes more demands on managers as they need to attract support for change internally and externally by engaging with stakeholders on the vision and form that change should take.

Forms of strategic change

According to Johnson and Scholes (1999), strategic change can take a number of forms dependent on why change is needed and what it is intended to achieve. They describe two forms of strategic change: incremental which is the main form of change and transformational which occurs less frequently. The form change takes will have its origins in the different organisational requirements and demands, and require a different response from those managing the change process. Whether change is incremental or transformational will depend largely on the pressures on the organisation from the external environment and the extent to which senior managers are aware of these pressures and respond strategically.

Figure 2.1: Types of strategic change

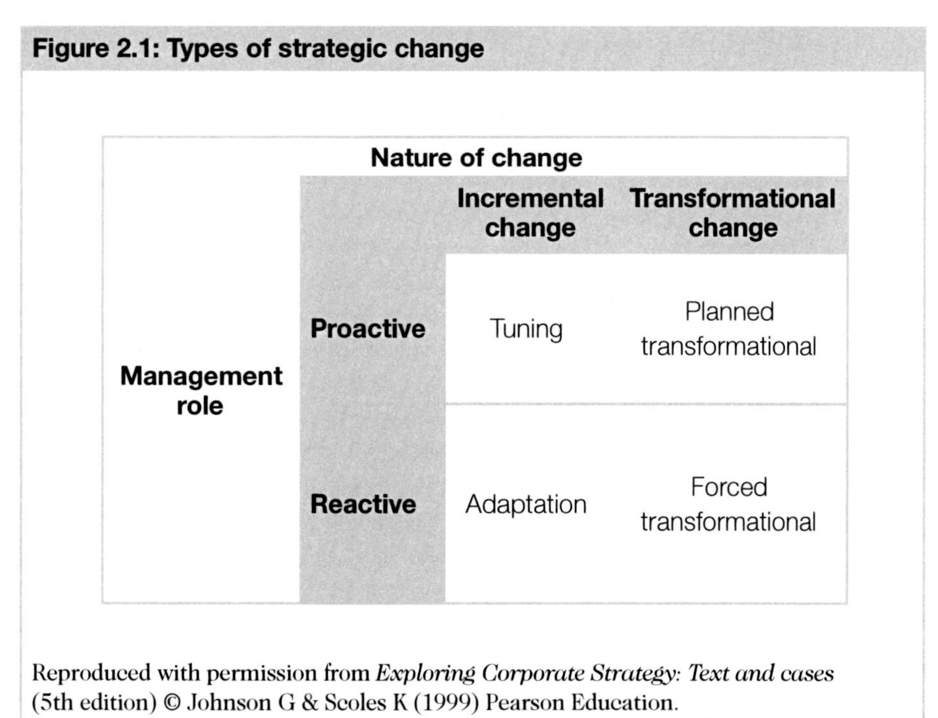

Reproduced with permission from *Exploring Corporate Strategy: Text and cases* (5th edition) © Johnson G & Scoles K (1999) Pearson Education.

Incremental change: proactive tuning and reactive adaptation

Johnson and Scholes (1999) argue that it is beneficial for organisations to change incrementally as this builds on the skills, routines and beliefs of staff so that change is likely to win their commitment. Incremental change is essentially about realigning the strategy of the organisation rather than fundamentally changing strategic direction with its consequent organisational upheaval. How incremental change is managed is also important and Johnson and Scholes suggest that proactive management is necessary if the organisation is to keep in touch with its environment and anticipate the need for change. This approach to incremental change is described as 'tuning' where current ways of operating are modified in response to pressures on the organisation that is recognised by managers. Where it is not possible to anticipate the need for change, but environmental pressures become apparent, managers may find themselves 'reacting' to pressures on the organisation and 'adapting' the organisation in response.

Both these forms of change take place within the existing paradigm of the organisation. That is the set of assumptions held in common by staff about the organisation and based on experience which has developed over time and becomes taken for granted (see Chapter 4 for further discussion of the paradigm). This can act as a powerful control on the organisation with the risk of strategic inertia or a reluctance to embrace new ideas even in the face of overwhelming evidence. Both 'proactive tuning' and 'reactive adaptation' are common forms of change in health and social care organisations and, where used, demonstrate that those responsible for managing a service are continually scanning the external environment and anticipating the need for change, although they do not fundamentally change the paradigm of the organisation and the deeply held beliefs of staff. Therefore, proactive tuning and reactive adaptation are based on the existing paradigm and conform to the notion of incremental change, but carry in them the dangers of strategic drift.

Case study

Change at a community hospital: an example of incremental strategic change

A community hospital with an operating theatre providing day surgery was felt by senior managers to be performing below its potential.

Following a review of the service, areas for improvement were identified in both structure and processes. Two previously separate areas of activity – the theatre and pre/post operative care – were brought together to improve co-ordination and efficiency. The theatre was also operating under capacity and a significant increase in activities was introduced. Other changes included appointing new staff and improving the management of staff. Following the changes, a post-operation infection audit, patient feedback and staff satisfaction were all positive and demonstrated the value of the changes made. This change had strategic consequences as it provided a basis for the further development of day surgery and other investigative activities.

Comment

This case study demonstrates the value of incremental change, where senior managers anticipated the need for change and the need to continuously improve the performance of the service. The change could be described as 'tuning', as managers recognised that change was necessary and built on existing skills and routines of staff, and where a valuable resource was under utilised that could achieve a higher level of activity.

The dangers of strategic drift

Strategic drift is the term used to describe a situation where an organisation over time gradually loses contact with the environmental forces that are outside its control. The main cause of strategic drift is the failure of those leading the organisation to recognise signs in the wider external environment that the organisation needs to change. Senior managers fail to frequently scan the external environment to identify whether the organisation is drifting from the direction it needs to take if it is to survive and prosper. When the environmental forces increase to a sufficient extent that change is inevitable, this can result in a need for transformational change if the organisation is to survive. There are risks that any changes implemented may not be sufficient to ensure that the organisation remains responsive to its environment. This can mean that incremental change is insufficient in the face of external pressures, and where there is a reluctance to challenge the existing paradigm of the organisation. As a result more radical change may become necessary as the organisation's performance continues to deteriorate or stakeholders press for urgent action.

Johnson and Scholes (1999) suggest some of the symptoms to look out for in the type of organisation that is susceptible to strategic drift.

- Organisation has a highly homogeneous culture with few differences of belief and assumptions about the organisation's place in the external world. There are well established routines that staff are not expected to deviate from.
- Little tolerance of questioning or challenge within the organisation; a readiness to dismiss new ideas, with an avoidance of debate of difficult or sensitive issues.
- Powerful blockages to change at the top of the organisation where senior managers are resistant to change has been described as the 'concrete ceiling'.
- Organisation has little focus on the external environment and tends to build its strategy around an internalised view of the world.
- Deteriorating performance that can only be detected by benchmarking against other successful organisations.

Figure 2.2: The risk of strategic drift

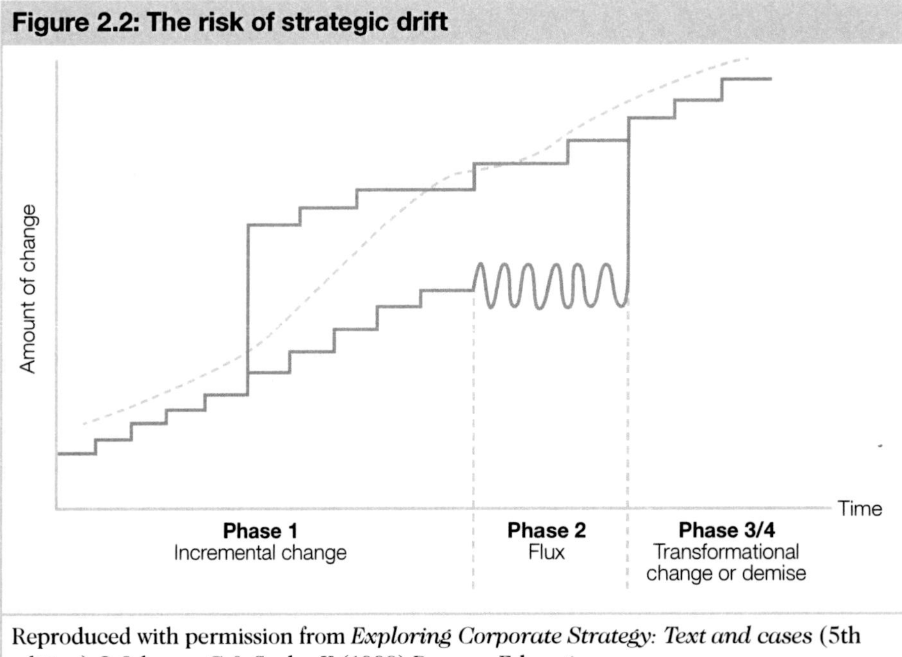

Reproduced with permission from *Exploring Corporate Strategy: Text and cases* (5th edition) © Johnson G & Scoles K (1999) Pearson Education.

The figure above describes the increasing gap between environmental change and the incremental change undertaken (phase 1). As the gap between the environment and the organisation increases, there is a state of flux (phase 2) with no clear direction or response, which further damages performance. Eventually, transformational change takes place, or the organisation declines or faces demise (phase 3/4).

Transformational change: planned and forced

We have seen how incremental change can offer advantages to the organisation in building on the skills and routines of staff, but because it is bounded by the paradigm and routines of the organisation, it may be insufficiently radical to respond to intense external pressures and also be susceptible to strategic drift. In these circumstances transformational change may be needed. Johnson and Scholes (1999) describe transformational change as change which cannot be handled within the existing paradigm and organisational routines, and may result from either a 'proactive planned' process of change or a 'reactive forced' change. The latter is likely if there has been significant strategic drift and resulted in a deterioration of performance, or external stakeholders demand a new strategic direction.

Planned transformational change takes place where managers anticipate the need for change by keeping in touch with both the internal and external environment and reacting to environmental pressures. Anticipating the need for change means that managers may have more time to react to the changes needed, and avoid being forced into change with all the costs of a sudden disruption to structures and processes. It also provides more time to communicate and consult with staff and explain the need for change. Even though managers may have more time to respond to the need for change it does not mean that implementation is necessarily straightforward as changes to structures, systems and processes will inevitably threaten the existing paradigm and deeply held beliefs about the organisation.

Where managers fail to see the need for strategic change, in time the only option may be forced transformational change. This is where pressures on the organisation become extreme and its continued survival may be threatened with managers having to react to events that are often outside their control due to extreme strategic drift. This change can be highly disruptive and painful as it can challenge deeply entrenched attitudes and beliefs, and result in strong resistance to attempts to change the organisation, which may only further delay the need for urgent change.

Transformational change, whether planned or forced fundamentally, changes an organisation in terms of its belief systems, power relations and activities (Matrix, 2006). It can mean a major shift in policy, or where an organisation is facing crisis it can be more wide-ranging and require the organisation to fundamentally change direction in order to survive, which in turn can challenge current ways of working.

Case study

Forced transformational change in a social services department

Following the joint review of a social services department, a report to the local authority described a series of fundamental shortcomings in the management and operation of the service. The service had a highly centralised management structure, which was cumbersome and stifled local initiative, with little devolved responsibility.

This structure, with its strong central control and financial stability, had been politically convenient, but at the expense of developing responsive services that had kept pace with changing need. At a practice level the provision had been inconsistent, with decisions about services dependent on individual workers' commitment and abilities. This was mirrored by a lack of response to the needs of service users, with a culture of paternalism described as 'doing to', rather than 'engaging with'. The authority had relied heavily on traditional residential care and day care, and had not developed more individualised services that supported service users in their own homes. There was poorly developed partnership working with the health service, and little consultation with the voluntary sector. Overall, the system did not ensure consistent and adequate standards of service. Following the review, the social services department implemented a series of radical changes including: appointing a new director and senior managers, a fundamental restructuring of its services, with the creation of adult and children's divisions and devolved responsibility to area managers.

Comment

This case study demonstrates the dangers facing an organisation when it fails to adapt to demands in the external environment and fails to develop its services in order to meet the needs of users. The dominant management style was one of central control, with little devolution of responsibility to the periphery of the organisation that was close to users. Consequently, it was less aware of the changing needs and did not empower its local managers to develop more sensitive services. The review described an organisation that was experiencing strategic drift and had failed to respond to changes in its external environment, both at a broad policy level and also in relation to the experiences and needs of service users.

Externally imposed change

Another form of forced change is where health and social care organisations have to respond to government policy initiatives that have a significant impact on the strategy and operation of services. These may impose demands on the organisation that have to be managed whether they require a reorganisation of structures or changes to professional practice. Government may dictate a particular course of action to follow, or insist on regulatory control, and this means that senior managers are less able to determine their own strategic control or direction, or implement their vision of the future. This does not mean that strategies are implemented in some crude top-down manner, as there will still be bargaining and negotiation between senior managers and external agencies, such as central government, about resources and the direction of strategy (Collier *et al*, 2001).

Managers at every level have to interpret what these changes mean for their service and its users. Government ministers, civil servants and senior managers tend to see change in broad terms and leave the detail for someone else to translate into practice. It is the translation into practice that is the hardest part! The difficulty of initiatives that come from outside the organisation is that staff are required to change the way they do things to comply with external demands that may have no internal logic, according to their perspective. This can undermine their sense of control and raises concerns about what the change will mean to their roles in the future. But even where changes are non-negotiable this does not mean that operations will necessarily change in the way that politicians or senior managers expect. Staff will not necessarily comply unquestioningly when asked to change their practice.

Professionals exercise personal initiative and are the gatekeepers of key resources, including the application of their own expertise and effort, and will have to be negotiated with to release these resources (Smale, 1998). Managers are required to ensure that staff follow new procedures or adopt new techniques and that there is an element of command and control in this approach, but managers still have to listen and discuss and invite feedback from staff on how the changes can be implemented. People are not machines and how they perform will depend, among other things, on how they respond to a manager's communication. This means that although managers are vested with the power to order behavioural compliance, staff may not internalise the required change and have the scope to subtly or radically change their practice from the instructed behaviour. In other words, what people actually do and what senior managers think they should do can be quite different things.

Corporate change programmes

Most large scale change in organisations is planned as a result of deliberate decisions usually driven from the top of the organisation. Senior managers set the agenda for change and plan, at least in outline, the stages of implementation. By contrast, change that is initiated from the bottom-up is the result of learning and adaptation by people who are directly involved in delivering a service. This is seen as a continuous process of learning from experience and adapting to changing circumstances. This approach to change contrasts with the tendency to place faith in corporate change programmes that often fail to deliver the changes promised. Research into the impact of these programmes by Beer *et al* (1990), such as culture change, quality circles and business process re-engineering, found that none had brought about any genuine change (see Chapter 3 for a case study of total quality management).

The difficulty these programmes pose is that they often offer standardised change packages that do not relate to the day-to-day realities of the organisation. The techniques promoted by consultants and trainers result in staff feeling frustrated as they are unable to apply the new techniques because the basic conditions in the organisation remain unchanged. This can have the opposite effect as these programmes can undermine individuals' commitment to change. This is not to say that the thinking behind these change techniques is wrong, it is rather that the techniques are often used in isolation to spread change throughout an organisation, where more effective change is often through long-term learning processes that improve individual practice and processes rather than quick fixes, no matter how attractive. What does work more effectively, according to Beer *et al*, is where senior managers encourage and support frontline staff to try new ways of working and are able to successfully communicate the effectiveness of change to other parts of the organisation.

Successful strategic change

Where change is successful there is likely to have been a close relationship between strategic and operational change processes and consensus about the purpose of change. Translating strategic change objectives into new operational processes requires detailed planning, supported by resources and key tasks identified supported by a range of personnel with change management roles. Failure to take account of the requirements of implementation at the operational level has been described as the 'Achilles heel' of strategic change, where senior managers fail to support the process of implementation that is essential to translate strategic intentions into new changed activities and behaviours at the front line. This also highlights the dangerous assumption that change can be decreed from the top and is likely to result in superficial compliance. This can see staff reverting to their old behaviours once the pressure for change is relaxed, if there is a failure to translate strategic aims into successful operational activity (Ferlie, 2003).

Operational change

Strategic change, by its very nature, can fundamentally change the purpose and direction of an organisation. Operational change, on the other hand, is concerned with the activities of those staff who manage or work at the front line and are intimately involved and familiar with organisational routines and processes. It is often described as 'bottom-up change' as it emanates from the bottom of the organisation, as opposed to change that is planned by senior managers from the top of the organisation. This form of change, rather than emanating from senior managers, involves adjustments to structures and processes, but does not involve fundamental change to the organisation's strategy (Matrix, 2006). Typically this can be seen in the work of managers and professionals who develop solutions to problems of practice as they arise, and usually originates within the organisation as staff recognise the need for change, whether this is the replacement of equipment that has become outdated, new procedures, or the need to update the skills of staff in the face of new demands. The value of operational change is that staff working at the front line are in a strong position to make changes under their control, or press for changes through consultation with senior managers based on their experience and understanding of the organisation and its processes.

Changes, which stem from an understanding of problems at the operational level, and use the experience of frontline managers and staff who are best placed to identify where processes are not working effectively, need to become routine and continuous.

Improvement has no end point if an organisation is to be well managed and sensitive to its internal and external environments. If improvement stops, atrophy and fossilisation occur (Brown, 1996). Operational change, with its continuous adjustments to systems, processes and structures, does not usually fundamentally change the strategy or core values of the organisation, or the work patterns of staff; it tends to be less resisted. Of course, the consequences of change can still lead to questioning and resistance by staff, particularly if it threatens well established work patterns or social relations built up over time and taken for granted by staff. But, by and large, routine changes are easier to implement as they do not threaten the beliefs held by staff about the purpose of the organisation. In this way ideas that are generated by staff are likely to be accepted more fully than those promoted by senior managers who can often be seen to be less sympathetic and less understanding of needs of frontline staff.

Case study

Change in a residential home: an example of operational change

Following an inspection by the regulator, a residential home for older people was found to have poor quality administrative procedures for recording routine activities, such as equipment testing and safety procedures. As a result, the home was given a lower quality rating with the risks to its image and reputation. This came as shock to the manager and staff of the home as they prided themselves on the high quality care provided to residents. The manager introduced a series of mandatory staff training sessions on the importance of accurate and timely recording of activities and simplified the forms and filing system to enable all staff to more easily record activities.

Comment

This case example demonstrates the need for managers to continually monitor the performance of their service where what are seen as routine administrative procedures can undermine the confidence of regulators in a service and harm its reputation.

The concept of emergent change also recognises the limitations of senior managers in prescribing the details of change. Child's (2005) view is that they should avoid getting involved in the details of change. Their role is to specify the general direction of change and generate a supportive climate for its implementation. Taking this approach they encourage ideas to emerge at a lower level and facilitate the process by providing vision, ensuring the necessary resources and support systems are in place, and reinforcing the commitment to newly emerged solutions in other parts of the organisation. Ideally, bottom-up pressure coincides with top-down concern, with both levels trying to achieve the same outcome. There is then a greater likelihood of successful implementation.

Although change at the operational level is the most common form of change as it tends to build on the skills, routines and beliefs of staff, it is more likely to win the commitment and support from staff affected by the change. This is not to say that incremental change is necessarily easy. It can still result in resistance by staff if they feel their established routines are threatened and much of the success will be dependent on the skills of those responsible for implementing change. This gradual change over time is natural and desirable and can avoid the need for the more radical change that is forced on an organisation where it may result in considerable internal disruption and less control over the outcome of change.

Figure 2.3: Strategic and operational change contrasted

Strategic change	Operational change
Led by senior managers	Led by frontline managers or professionals
Focus on mission and strategy	Focus on operational procedures
Can mean culture and value change	Culture unaffected
May require radical shift in behaviour	Adaptation to current behaviour
Long-term	Short-term
Risk of unintended consequences	Predictable
Requires long-term persistence	Quickly implemented
Systems change	Within existing systems
Potential for high resistance	Low resistance

The wider impact of change

At whatever level it is initiated, whether it is strategic change affecting the whole organisation, or operational change in a particular department or affecting individual roles, it is likely to have a wider impact. Child (2005) argues that it is artificial to separate out areas and levels of change as organisational systems are so interdependent that change in one part is likely to have knock-on effects elsewhere. He suggests that wherever change starts it has the potential to influence how an organisation performs, and this points to the value of identifying the best place to start change. When organisations are in difficulty there is a tendency to launch radical change programmes, particularly organisational restructuring which can be insufficiently responsive to changing conditions in organisations. This can be seen in numerous organisation-wide change programmes in public services that have a poor record and have failed to deliver the anticipated changes. An alternative proposed by Child (2005) is to initiate a focused approach that addresses a particular problem and to use the experience gained as the impetus for subsequent change in other parts of the organisation. This approach can serve as an experimental pilot for subsequent wider developments and demonstrates the potential benefits of organisational change.

Shared commitment and organisational learning

What this exploration of strategic and operational change points to is the complexity of change in health and social care organisations. It is naïve to assume a linear movement of change from strategy to implementation as this fails to take into account the views and opinions of a wide range of people likely to be involved in any major change. As Smale (1998) reminds us, all this points to the need for management approaches that are more sophisticated than assuming that simply telling people to do something differently will lead to a change in behaviour. If managers want to create the potential for change then it helps if there is a convergence of views, and where there is a divergence, that this is made transparent and openly discussed. There is likely to be much greater convergence of ideas where organisations are responsive to change as a result of a shared commitment to continually improving performance, which is typically found in organisations that are less hierarchical and characterised by open communication across different disciplines or groups. Kanter (1985) describes these as 'integrative' organisations which encourage and enable staff to innovate, and 'segregated' ones that block initiatives and stifle innovation.

Much of what Smale (1998) and Kanter (1985) are describing is found in the notion of the learning organisation, where staff are encouraged to share information and knowledge in order to respond creatively to changes occurring around them, particularly in the external environment and contributing to the identification of opportunities that are necessary for the future health of the organisation. This contrasts with organisations with rigid hierarchical structures and managers who have vested interests in rejecting any ideas that do not originate from senior layers of the organisation, which stifles the release of creativity. Where an organisation learns by continually questioning itself it is more likely to modify its strategies and assumptions (which govern staff behaviour) in ways that are healthy. Johnson and Scholes (1999) argue that the collective knowledge of all the individuals in an organisation usually exceeds what the organisation itself 'knows' and is capable of doing. Management's role is to encourage processes that enable individuals to share information and knowledge, and with the absence of power tactics and blocking routines it should be possible to create a shared vision of the future that can be reinforced by the mutual support of the organisation's staff.

Summary

This chapter has described a range of approaches to change. These can be either strategic or operational. Strategic is where the change is wide ranging and can fundamentally change an organisation, whether planned or forced, and is usually led by senior managers. Operational involves changes to processes and procedures that are mainly the responsibility of frontline managers and staff who are in a strong position to decide how to most effectively bring about a change in practice. It is the linking of strategic change with operational change that is critical for effectively realising organisational strategy. Whichever form change takes, the risks of strategic drift are ever present. Change can also be forced on organisations which can severely limit managers' potential to develop their own strategic direction, and result in difficult negotiations with staff who have to comply with change agendas where they have little opportunity for participation. We have also seen that senior managers, in their search for solutions to organisational problems, can place undue optimism on the potential of programme change initiatives, which are often unsuccessful due to their incompatibility with the organisation's norms and processes. Lastly, change is seen to have greater potential for success if there is a convergence of views and a shared understanding about the need for change, and points to the importance of the attributes of the learning organisation, with its focus on the knowledge and creativity of everyone in the organisation contributing to its success.

References

Alford J (2001) The implications of 'publicness' for strategic management theory. In: G Johnson & K Scholes (Eds) *Exploring Public Sector Strategy*. Harlow: Pearson Education.

Beer M, Eisenstat RA & Spector B (1990) *The Critical Path to Corporate Renewal*. Boston: Harvard Business School Press.

Brown J (1996) *Chance Favours the Prepared Mind*. London: HSMO.

Child J (2005) *Organization: Contemporary principles and practice*. Oxford: Blackwell Publishing.

Collier N, Fishwick F & Johnson G (2001) The processes of strategy development in the public sector. In: G Johnson & K Scholes (Eds) *Exploring Public Sector Strategy*. Harlow: Pearson Education.

Ferlie E (2003) General Principles of Change. *Newsletter, Issue 10, January*. London: The Association of Research Ethics Committees.

Johnson G & Scholes K (1999) *Exploring Corporate Strategy: Text and cases* (5th edition). London: Pearson Education.

Kanter RM (1985) *The Change Masters: Corporate entrepreneurs at work*. London: Allen and Unwin.

Matrix (2006) *What is transformational change?* London: Matrix Research and Consultancy Ltd.

Pugh D (1993) Understanding and managing organizational change. In: C Mabey. & B Mayon-White (Eds) *Managing Change* (2nd edition). London: Paul Chapman Publishing.

Smale G (1998) *Managing Change Through Innovation*. London: HMSO.

Chapter 3

A contextual approach to change

Key points

- The importance of context in organisational change
- The context, process and content as a way of understanding how change progresses in organisations
- The value of identifying the receptive and non-receptive contexts for change
- Research studies of health care illustrate the value of understanding the contextual factors in change

Introduction

In order to understand the environment where change takes place it is helpful to draw on theories of organisational change which place events in their wider context. The work of Pettigrew *et al* (1992) who carried out one of the most extensive research projects into change in health care organisations is important. This research established why some organisations were better able than others to manage strategic change. The purpose of this research was to bridge the gap between the researchers and those managing change through detailed feedback to the organisations participating in the study on why some of them were more receptive to change than others. This chapter will describe the model of strategic change and some of the implications for managers who are crafting strategy or tasked with implementation at the front line.

The context, process and content of change

The research of Pettigrew *et al* (1992) starts from the assumption that it is not sufficient to have the correct policies for change, but that organisations need the organisational capacity for change, which in turn can translate the change agenda into practice. The change agenda which had seen the radical transformation of both acute and long-term care services required a broad range of political and management skills that were not achieved by simplistic models of rational processes and top-down directives. The contextual model recognises the complexity of change, and that there is a continuous interplay between the 'context' of change, the 'process' of change and the 'content' of change. It is how these three areas are managed that is critical to effective change.

Figure 3.1: Three dimensions of change

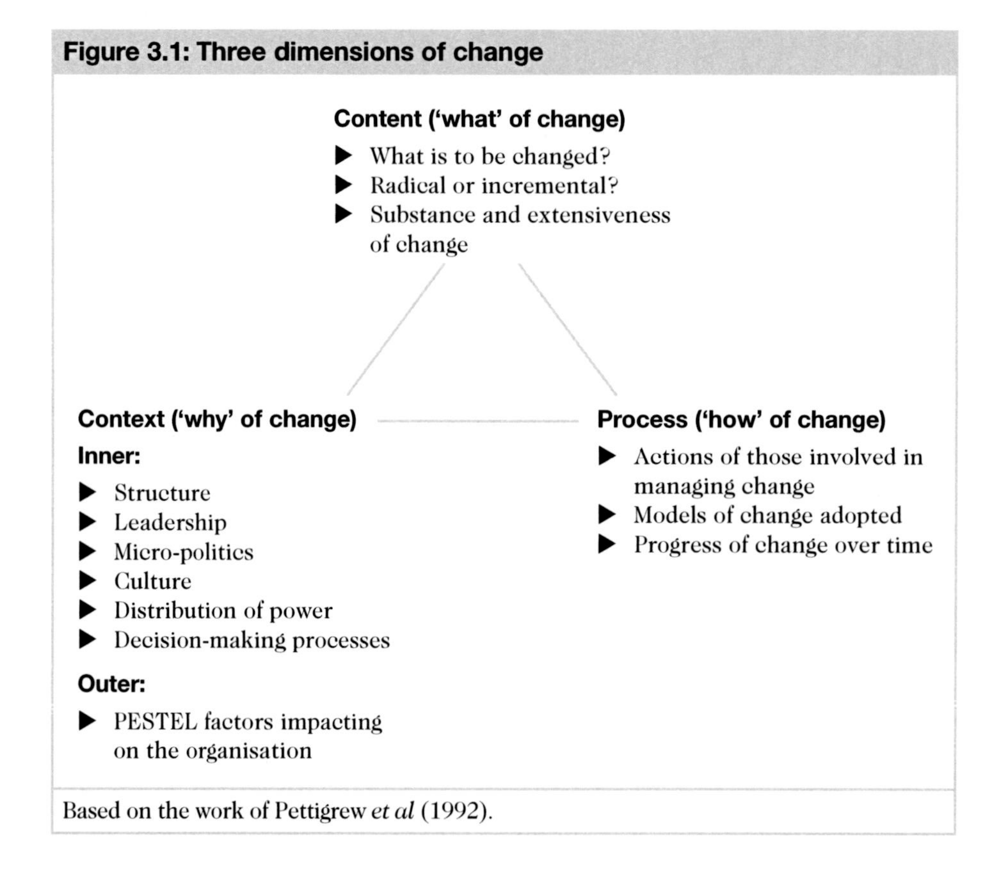

Based on the work of Pettigrew *et al* (1992).

The context or 'why' of change

This is divided into the outer and inner context. The outer context refers to the political and social context of the organisation, as well as national policies for health and social care services. Many of the external factors have been described in Chapter 1 in the analysis of external drivers found in the use of the PESTEL technique. The inner context refers to the strategies, structure, culture, politics and management process through which change has to proceed. An understanding of the outer context enables managers to analyse the national and local barriers to implementing change. An understanding of the inner context is useful in helping to predict those contexts that will be receptive to change and those that may inhibit change.

The process or 'how' of change

This refers to the actions, reactions and interactions of those involved in the change process as they seek to move the organisation from its present to its future state. Here, the role of powerful interest groups and influential individuals, both within and outside the organisation, is important in understanding how change can be planned. The wide range of stakeholders likely to be involved or affected by strategic change is significant (see Chapter 8 for a discussion on stakeholding). Each will have their own perspectives on the proposals, along with conflicting concerns and expectations that can strongly influence the success of a proposed course of action.

The content or 'what' of change

This refers to the particular area of transformation that the organisation is seeking to achieve. Some changes will involve the radical restructuring of services, others will be the incremental growth of new services, or there may be technological changes or changes to roles. It is the substance and extensiveness of change that needs to be considered. Each will have uncertainty and risks attached.

The value of this model of change is in understanding the importance of the interaction of the three components – content, context and process. It treats change in a more holistic and dynamic manner rather than just focusing on separate elements in a change process. The model sees successful change as a result of the interaction of the three elements, in which each element can influence the other.

Receptive contexts for change

In analysing why some health service organisations achieved a higher rate of change than others, Pettigrew *et al* (1992) asked the question 'why was the rate and pace of strategic change different across different organisations?'. The pace of change was found in the interplay between context, content and the process of change, with the context the critical shaper in the process of change. This led Pettigrew *et al* to develop the model of the receptive and non-receptive contexts for change. What the notion of receptivity demonstrated was that some health care organisations showed different levels of receptivity for change than others. Some contexts seemed favourably associated with forward movement, whereas others appeared to be associated with blocks on change. These were dependent on a range of factors, particularly in the inner context, and referred to such issues as: sustained leadership from the top of the organisation, a multidisciplinary leadership team, the commitment of key professionals and good relations between managerial and clinical groups, as examples of where strategic change was more effective.

Receptivity factors

In Pettigrew *et al*'s (1992) research, eight factors served to differentiate the higher and lower performers and provided a linked set of conditions which provided high energy around change.

1. **Quality and coherence of local policy**. This factor is concerned with the quality of strategy formulation following analysis of data, with testing of initial thoughts and coherence between goals to ensure that the new policy is feasible. A broad vision rather than a specific blueprint for change was seen to have benefits as it enabled commitment building and allowed interest groups to buy into the change process, with top-down and bottom-up pressure converging. The broad vision then enabled more detailed plans to be developed later as different parts of the organisation began the process of implementation.
2. **Key people leading change**. This factor is concerned with the availability of key people in critical posts who lead change. This is less about one individual, but rather a more pluralistic leadership with managers and professionals from different constituencies providing complementary skills and assets. Leadership is seen as a collective, complementary and multi-faceted approach to leading change. Stability and continuity is seen as important, with dangers that the movement of key personnel can drain energy and commitments from the change process. Key people may not always be associated so much with posts and hierarchical level, rather with personality than formal status or rank, and who have the commitment and skills needed to develop new services.
3. **Co-operative inter-organisational networks**. This factor is concerned with the importance of inter-organisational networks, for example, between the NHS, local government and voluntary organisations. This recognises that any one organisation is often insufficient to bring about change. Co-operation is increased where there are individuals who span different organisational boundaries (health authority members who are also on social care committees) can enrich these networks. Other factors strengthening

co-operation include joint posts and liaison posts, and joint training to reduce inter-professional disputes. The research suggested that the strongest networks were often the most informal ones, where trust and open communication had been established over time. Networks were nevertheless vulnerable when key individuals moved as successors may have different interests.

4. **Supportive organisational culture**. This factor is concerned with the building of organisational cultures that support strategic change. This is a difficult area (see Chapter 4) as changing cultures is notoriously complex as organisations are not a single culture, but can be a collection of subcultures. Cultures are also deep seated assumptions and values, beliefs and behaviours that can make change difficult, create inertia and generate considerable resistance. Nevertheless cultures do change over time and can be influenced by a strong value base articulated by leaders who communicate their commitment to change. Culture is also seen to change as a result of the appointment of new leaders and the introduction of new symbols and language.
5. **Environmental pressure that was moderate, predictable and long-term**. This is concerned with the role of environmental pressure that leads to triggering radical change. Too much pressure can deflect or drain energy out of organisational systems, as well as stimulating change. An example of the way financial pressures can result in managers fire fighting and produce paralysis and loss of control, demonstrates how pressure can threaten rather than act as a stimulus to change.
6. **Simplicity and clarity of goals and priorities**. This is concerned with senior managers' ability to identify a small set of key priorities and to insulate these from the continual short-term pressures that are a feature of health care organisations. There is also the danger that too many priorities mean that they become meaningless. Examples of where there are long-term changes that require considerable behavioural adaptation and are dependent on networks of widespread units are far more difficult and onerous to implement.
7. **Positive patterns of managerial–clinical relations**. This factor is concerned with the quality of relationships between managers, clinicians and other professionals, recognising that these relationships can be a stimulant or block to change. The value of seeking common ground between managers and professionals, involving clinicians early on in the planning stage and working to build a climate of trust, honesty and effective communication are all seen as critical to successful change. Where managers understand what clinicians value and where clinicians think strategically and managerially, then more effective working relationships are achieved.
8. **Fit between the change agenda and the locality**. This factor is concerned with the locality of a service and can have an impact on how easy it is to achieve change. For the NHS organisations studied, the degree of co-terminosity with

social services departments, the nature of the local NHS workforce, whether there is a teaching hospital present and the strength and nature of the local political climate are all important factors. Some of these are recognised as being beyond the control of managers, although an awareness of their influence is important in anticipating potential obstacles to change.

Figure 3.2: Receptivity contexts for change – the eight factors

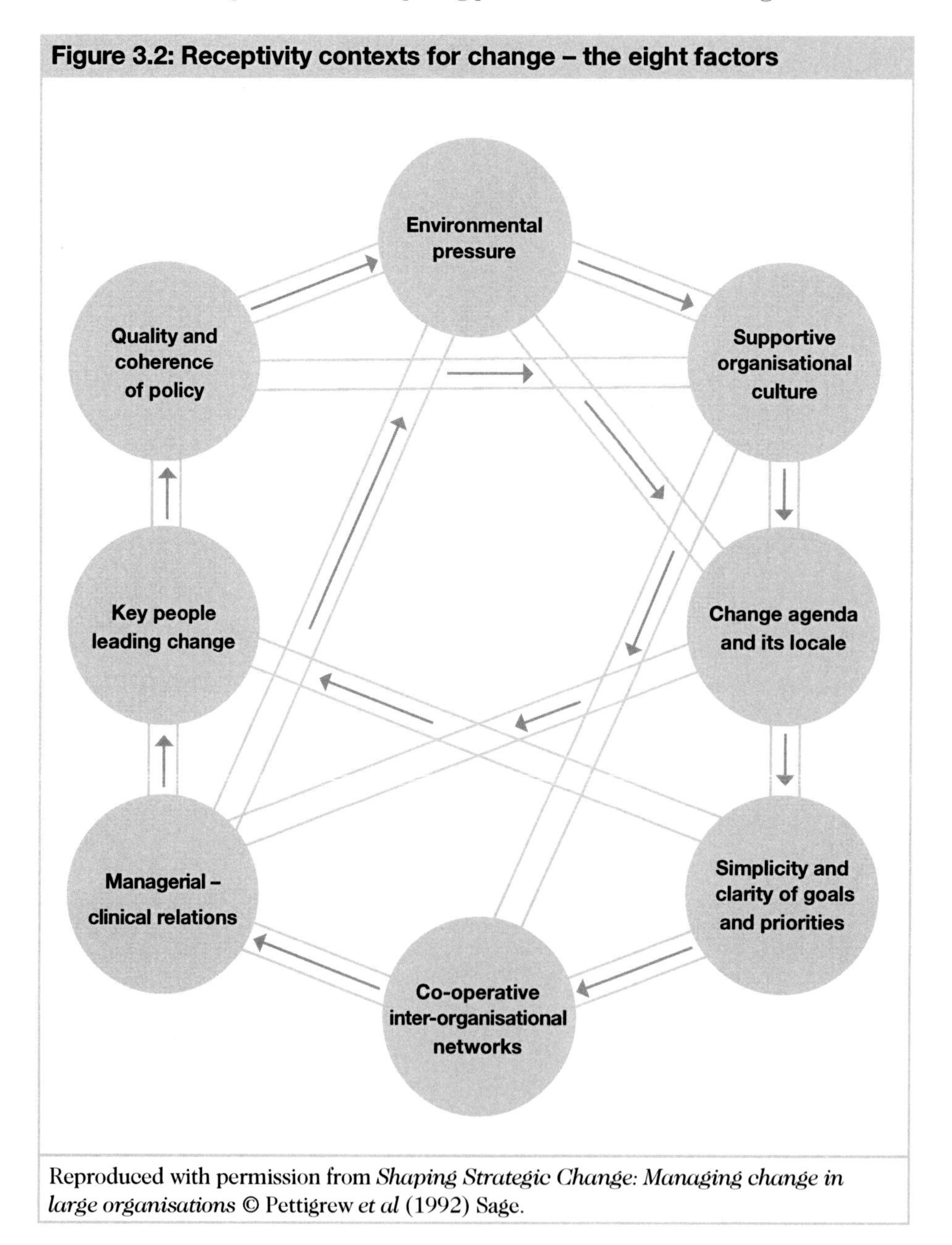

Reproduced with permission from *Shaping Strategic Change: Managing change in large organisations* © Pettigrew *et al* (1992) Sage.

Innovation and change in response to HIV/AIDS

Subsequent research by Bennett and Ferlie (1994), using a contextualist approach, studied the organisational responses to HIV/AIDS by district health authorities in a range of geographical locations. This research demonstrated how receptivity factors influenced the provision of services which were led initially by clinicians rather than managers, with change 'emergent' rather than planned or managed. This was understandable as the crisis was seen as a health issue rather than a financial one, with external pressure both from government and local action groups.

In summarising the receptivity factors we can see many similarities with the earlier research of Pettigrew *et al* (1992) in that a series of 'signs and symptoms' of receptivity were present and associated with the speed of change that took place in the provision of services in response to the HIV/AIDS crisis.

First, there was intense external pressure on services from the top-down in the form of government demands for action, coupled with bottom-up pressure from local action groups. Second, there was a strong 'fit' between the teaching hospitals and their expertise and the strength of the local action groups. Third, there developed a shared 'HIV culture' which, included clinicians, managers and local action groups, which energised and facilitated inter-organisational co-operation. Fourth, the key people leading change were the clinicians, with managers playing a secondary role. Over time a wider range of people were mobilised with teams and networks emerging to facilitate change.

Fifth, HIV/AIDS as a single issue enabled a focus on the 'mission' in a much clearer sense than in other large scale change projects. Many of those involved early on, and who played change champion roles, sustained their interest over the long term and their commitment to the service was enduring. Sixth, again the importance of inter-organisational networks was seen as critical, with evidence from the research suggesting that informal networks played a significant role in supporting joint working. The researchers found a high degree of informal co-operation at clinical level driven, and influenced to some extent, by ideologically informed professionals, and working effectively in spite of, rather than because of, formal decision-making systems. Seventh, the effectiveness of managerial and clinical relations was seen as important in supporting the development of responses to the crisis and establishing services.

As in the earlier research, there was a wide range of patterns with managers and clinicians leading in some services, and clinicians in others. The role of public health physicians was important as they became the 'nominated physicians' as required by government to cover the HIV/AIDS issue, and some were particularly effective in promoting a community, as opposed to a narrow acute sector care, although others in similar posts took less interest and left it to clinicians to develop responses. The eighth and final factor concerned the quality and coherence of policy. The picture varied across the different localities with loose central policy guidance providing opportunities for interested authorities to develop their own strategic framework, particularly where this was supported by local epidemiological data. Whereas other localities had greater difficultly framing policy, lacked good quality data, and in some cases became overwhelmed by the pace of change on the ground.

What this later study demonstrated was the importance of understanding the context for change, with the eight 'signs and symptoms' identified in the original study by Pettigrew *et al* (1992) remaining valid in this later study and providing evidence that there are generic processes at work in shaping patterns of strategic change, at least in health service contexts.

Case study

Total quality management in a district health authority

To demonstrate the value of the contextual approach, a case study of a total quality management (TQM) initiative in a district health authority illustrates aspects of the Pettigrew model in analysing strategic change (Scragg, 2001). Between 1989 and 1993, the district implemented a series of top-down initiatives that attempted to fundamentally transform the service with the introduction of general management, quality management and subsequently internal market reforms. At the outset, TQM was part of a government drive to transfer private sector techniques into the NHS with the influence of the 'quality movement' being a key factor (Joss & Kogan, 1995). The intention was to bring about a radical change in the organisational culture, which would be more attuned to the laws of the marketplace, and was more responsive to consumers and their preferences. Staff would be taught to use quality techniques which would improve the efficiency of the service and as a result be better able to meet the requirements of patients. These external drivers constituted a powerful outer context for change.

The opportunity to become a demonstration site for TQM coincided with a series of actions in the district which were the internal drivers for change. The introduction of general management – with the appointment of a new general manager and new senior managers and the promotion of a managerial culture – a growing interest in consumerism, and a district general manager with an interest in quality that predated the initiative, demonstrated an internal context that was receptive to change, at least at senior management level. This internal context was reinforced by the appointment of a management consultant who had worked on earlier quality management projects in the private sector, and a newly appointed training manager who became the 'change agent' and led the initiative with senior management sponsorship.

An important change at this period was the perception about the responsibility for quality. This had previously been seen as the preserve of clinicians with little management involvement or interest. The drive to introduce greater consumerism into the NHS increasingly saw managers taking more responsibility for quality, at least for those areas they could directly influence, such as hotel services. Although a range of new initiatives were introduced into the district's units these mainly focused on non-clinical areas. In spite of considerable work with clinicians, the quality techniques did not significantly influence clinical areas and quality remained in separate spheres of influence. This was mainly as a result of clinicians' resistance to TQM, which was seen as a business model and a 'foreign import' that was irrelevant to their work, and also concern about managers moving onto the 'turf' of what had been the exclusive territory of clinicians.

A further problem facing the initiative was the attitude of staff to TQM at a time when there was growing anxiety about government intentions for the service. The TQM initiative came at a time when there was increasing pressure as the gap between needs and resources became more acute (the district had experienced ward closures due to financial pressures), with professionals concerned about the future direction of the service, fuelled by government rhetoric which trumpeted the virtues of business and the market, resulting in fears of job losses or at least enforced changes of role and relocation as the internal market reforms dug more deeply into the service.

It was against this background that the team leading the TQM demonstration site had difficulty in persuading staff to adopt quality techniques. This also had all the hallmarks of an over-mechanistic transfer of ideas from the business sector into a service dominated by professional groups with their strong value base and culture that was resistant to change. The district, in effect, signed up to a detailed blueprint, typical of programmatic change models promoted by the external management consultant, at a time when staff were increasingly suspicious of change.

Nevertheless, some improvements did take place as a result of TQM. For example, environmental changes that were badly needed to shabby buildings following a lack of government investment over many years. New equipment was purchased which improved the performance of support staff, and some limited examples of multidisciplinary working methods were used to solve longstanding problems, albeit without the contribution of clinicians in most departments. Some elements of TQM were also adopted by managers and nursing staff in the community unit, which were later successfully used to develop the community care trust's quality policy. This trust was, importantly, less dependent on clinicians as service leaders, where clinicians were also less influential in terms of treatment regimes.

The demise of TQM in the district took place in a rapidly changing organisational environment with the publication of *Working for Patients* (DH, 1989) and the introduction of the *Patients Charter* (Cabinet Office, 1991). The changing political priorities at government and Department of Health level meant that the demonstration site went into rapid decline. The escalating weight of new initiatives following *Working for Patients* meant that managers had new priorities and this led to the TQM initiative being submerged by these competing demands. This period also saw the rapid separation of acute and community units prior to trust status, which saw declining support for TQM demonstration sites. These changes along with the reduced support for TQM saw the loss of a number of senior managers and the change agent which weakened the team that had responsibility for driving the TQM programme.

Comment

This case study highlights the complexity of introducing a strategic change initiative where the internal and external context have such a significant influence on both the change strategy and how it is received internally, and the power of external factors to undermine it. It is also evident that there was a range of non-receptive factors that was a substantial block on change. The enthusiastic commitment from a small group of senior managers, the change agent and management consultant did initially make progress and built a small coalition around change, but critically this did not include clinicians. Second, the TQM model was developed originally in a business environment and its philosophy and techniques did not transfer easily to the NHS, with its long history and powerful professional subcultures. Adapting quality techniques to health care organisations is also more complex than improving processes in manufacturing, which is the birthplace of TQM (Ovretveit, 2005). Third, the changes came at a time when the service felt assailed by political changes and staff were wary of any new initiatives which might threaten their jobs. Finally, the rapidly changing situation, with the introduction of new internal market structures and competing quality initiatives such as the *Patients Charter*, swamped TQM and led to its rapid demise. A more fruitful approach may have been to adopt some of the techniques of quality management and test these out in practice without attempting an organisation-wide change programme. This was evidenced in the community unit which successfully adopted some of the techniques of TQM to develop their own quality policies and practices.

Identifying what influences progress in change

More recent research for the Department of Health (Fitzgerald *et al*, 2006), which again highlighted the importance of the context for change, examined the management of service improvements in cancer, maternity and diabetes care and sought to understand how managers influence the effectiveness of change in services. The findings from these research sites demonstrated the importance of the complex interplay of factors in the local context and the roles and interactions of key people involved in service improvements.

Summary of findings

There were nine main findings in this research.

1. The local context was critical in understanding the potential for change. A cluster of factors such as past mergers, local networks and senior management commitment have a strong influence on the progress of service improvement. There was a positive history of prior change which had generated trust and created a co-operative culture with service and senior managers not being distracted by other agendas. There was change leadership at senior, executive and clinical service levels and this was dispersed across the organisation with good inter-professional relationships creating a strong foundation for change and no vacancies in key service improvement posts.

2. Competing agendas could distract from service improvements. When senior managers' attention was concentrated on externally imposed targets or structural change they were likely to distract from clinical service improvement. This finding suggested that externally imposed change can hamper the development of clinical services.

3. On a pessimistic note, the research found an increase in the number of staff who were in hybrid roles. These roles spanned clinical and managerial tasks, with managers focusing on operational rather than strategic management and little attention given to service improvement or change management. The question raised by these findings is whether the targets for these managers are achievable or their workload manageable.

4. The research found that staff in bridging roles can help drive forward change. These were mainly in hybrid roles which offered the opportunity to move between managerial and clinical areas, and as such were seen as critical in change. Other staff who have positions where they provide oversight across a PCT, such as advisers or facilitative roles in networks, can also play this role.

5. The importance of solid inter-professional relationships between clinicians and general managers was seen as important in service improvement, which recognised the complexity of change in multi-professional organisations such as health care. The researchers also found that good communication across primary and acute care networks achieved better outcomes for service users in the clinical areas studied. The research cautioned that existing networks could be either predominantly clinical or managerial, with the risk that decisions about service improvement processes could be one-sided.

6. Where the research sites appeared most receptive and proactive in improving services there was evidence of 'dispersed' leadership of change. This is a new pattern of leadership where there is the active involvement of staff at different levels in the organisation and from a range of professional

and managerial backgrounds. Where the sites had the most effective service improvements, small groups of managers worked together, consulting each other and having respect for each other's viewpoints.

7. With one or two exceptions the HR function played little part in supporting change. It was distanced from clinical activity and HR specialists were rarely seen to play a part in facilitating change. With the development of new roles and working methods to achieve service improvements, HR needed to play a more supportive role. HR was seen to have the potential to play a much larger role in supporting change and developing leaders of change. Similarly, it could also play a role in relationship building and the resolution of disputes.
8. The research found differences between primary and acute care, particularly in relation to their structures and resource capacity. At the time of the research PCTs were in a state of transition with new tasks, relationships and systems still to be put in place. This was stretching management and clinical staff too thinly over too many issues, and improvements in primary care appeared fragile and based on too few committed people.
9. Overall, the research found that a combination of contextual factors and individual behaviours was crucial to progress in service improvement. The complex interaction between all the above factors meant that some combinations led to positive progress, while others had a negative impact.

The message from different research studies is reinforced by Hardy (1987) who, although discussing change in higher education, supports the view that it is the crucial importance of the interplay of content of change, the processes of change and the context that produces the outcomes that determine the success of a strategic change initiative. Any significant strategic change involves the ability to sustain high levels of morale and commitment, which is influenced by the content, process and context. This requires senior managers to understand the relationship between these three components and who has the necessary skills to manage them. Hardy argues that the key to success is matching the content of a strategy with the process of implementation that is consistent with the particular organisational context.

Summary

The value of using a contextual approach to change is its usefulness in alerting managers to issues of importance when they are engaged in strategic change. Research by Pettigrew *et al* (1992) and Bennett and Ferlie (1994) suggests there are generic components to strategic change processes in health care and that a contextual approach has application across a wide range of organisations. This is further reinforced by the findings of research by Fitzgerald *et al* (2006). These research studies do not offer simple solutions to the introduction and management of change, but rather they increase awareness of the importance of the context which may be receptive or unreceptive in which change occurs, and the importance of understanding the process through which change has to travel. The case study points to a number of contextual factors which made it difficult to introduce quality management into the acute trust, and it illustrates the wider issues of corporate change programmes that are not sensitively tailored to the organisation. All change programmes, where they require the co-operation of professionals, need to be sufficiently long-term, adequately resourced, and not in competition with other programmes or initiatives.

References

Bennett C & Ferlie E (1994) *Managing Crisis and Change in Health Care: Organizational response to HIV/AIDS*. Buckingham: Open University Press.

Cabinet Office (1991) *Patients Charter.* London: HMSO.

Department of Health (1989) *Working for Patients*. London: The Stationery Office.

Fitzgerald L, Lilley C, Addicott R, McGiven G & Buchanan D (2006) *Managing Change and Role Enactment in the Professionalised Organisation* [online]. London: NCCSDO, London School of Hygiene and Tropical Medicine. Available at: http://www.sdo.nihr.ac.uk/files/project/21-final-report.pdf (accessed June 2010).

Hardy C (1987) Using content, context, and process to manage university cutbacks. *The Canadian Journal of Higher Education* **17** (1) 65–82.

Joss R & Kogan M (1995) *Advancing Quality Management in the National Health Service*. Buckingham: Open University Press.

Ovretveit J (2005) Public service improvement. In: E Ferlie, LE Lynn & C Pollitt (Eds) *The Oxford Handbook of Public Management*. Oxford: Oxford University Press.

Pettigrew A, Ferlie EB & McKee L (1992) *Shaping Strategic Change: Making change in large organisations: the case of the National Health Service*. London: Sage.

Scragg T (2001) *Strategic Change in Context: A case study of a total quality management initiative in the National Health Service*. PhD thesis: University of Southampton.

Chapter 4

The power of culture

Key points

- Organisational culture plays a critical role in the management of change
- There are different approaches to understanding culture
- Central to culture is the paradigm and its influence on organisations
- The cultural web can help us understand how organisational activities and routines influence change
- Culture influences the socialisation of individuals in organisations

Introduction

This chapter will introduce the concept of organisation culture and its importance in the management of change. The chapter describes what is meant by organisational culture and how it impacts on organisations and why culture change can be a complex and challenging process. Organisational culture is a contested area of organisational theory, but one which is important for the leader to understand as it can have a significant influence on any attempt to introduce change in organisations. It is not uncommon, following revelation of poor quality services, to hear a plea that there must be 'an entire culture change in the way people are treated'. In spite of such pleas, often little appears to change. Greater knowledge of the power of organisational culture can help understand why managers of services fail to modernise their practices, even when new policy initiatives, research findings or models of good practice present overwhelming evidence for change. Some recent examples of poor quality services that have been investigated and reported publicly will be used to illustrate issues of organisational culture.

What are organisational cultures?

One of the problems in discussing organisational culture is that it can be difficult to define or explain precisely, and consequently difficult to change. Staff working in health and social care services may not be consciously aware of the culture of their workplace, even though it has a pervasive influence over their behaviour and actions. Culture is formed from a collection of traditions, values, policies, beliefs and attitudes that prevail throughout an organisation (Pettinger, 2000). It is best described as the deep-seated beliefs held by staff about the way they work, how work should be organised and how staff are controlled and rewarded within a particular organisation. This culture is consistently shared by a number of people about the service and is often described more simply as 'the way we do things around here'.

It encompasses the climate and atmosphere surrounding an organisation and the prevailing attitudes within it, including standards, morale and general attitudes. Harrison and Stokes (1992) go further and describe culture as those aspects of an organisation that give it a particular climate or feel, and that it is to an organisation what personality is to an individual, and helps distinguish one organisation from another. From these descriptions we can see that cultures can be a powerful source of influence and control in organisations.

Another perspective on culture is to examine the work of Meyerson and Martin (1987) who describe three models for understanding organisational culture.

1. **The integration model**. This sees culture as something that an organisation possesses and is recognisable and consistent across the organisation. This model sees culture as something which promotes integration across an organisation and can be manipulated to enhance integration. This is often a view held by senior managers who tend to see the organisation having a dominant or uniform culture which is susceptible to change as a result of management action. It is seen in the assumptions often made by managers that all staff in the organisation share their view of the need for a particular change.

2. **The difference model**. This sees culture as more pluralistic, with different cultures held by different interest groups within the same organisation. As a result of the different cultures it may be more difficult to develop joint activity or greater integration between groups. This is a view typically held by different professional groups who see their own part of the service as having a distinctly different culture than others. For example, different clinical or professional groups within the NHS who use their own professions as reference points.

3. **The ambiguity model**. This sees culture as something that is distinctively local and personal and is continually negotiated and renegotiated by individuals and groups in an organisation. Here individuals within an organisation can share some views in common, but disagree about others. As a result culture is constantly changing as individuals renegotiate their relationships with each other. This is seen in services where different professionals are negotiating their roles and relationships with each other and no integrated or interest group has established a dominant culture. Examples of research in newly established multidisciplinary mental health services come to mind here (Scragg, 2006).

Three layers of culture

One way of helping to make sense of the complex world of culture is to imagine the organisation as having three layers of culture with outer, middle and inner layers. Several writers have described this approach, including Schein (2004), and McAuley and Shanahan (1994). Using this model (see Figure 4.1 on p.62) as an example can help you make more sense of your own organisation's culture.

The three layers are:

- **Outer:** comprises artefacts and products, for example buildings, symbols, office layouts and dress codes that can be easily observed.
- **Middle:** encompasses the norms and values of the service that are demonstrated through attitudes and behaviours, verbal or written statements, particularly by influential people.
- **Inner:** comprises the basic assumptions commonly held by a workgroup and often unconscious. Schein refers to this as the essence of culture, which is more difficult to access and hard to recognise within and only uncovered through in-depth studies of organisations.

Can culture be managed?

A central issue in studies of organisational culture is whether it can be 'managed', and is therefore susceptible to change as a result of management intervention. Some researchers believe that organisations are cultures and therefore less susceptible to change. Others believe that organisations have cultures, and that the manifestations of culture are socially constructed, and therefore amenable to change (Ogbonna, 1993). It is also suggested that organisations are made up of a number of sub-cultures, whereas other researchers see organisations having a dominant culture (Johnson & Scholes, 2002). Whatever viewpoint we adopt, it is clear from research that changing a culture can be a long and potentially difficult process. Much will depend on the strength of the culture, the degree to which the organisation is threatened by external forces (for example, a damning report on the standards of service provided by external regulators), and the extent of change required if the organisation is to improve its practices significantly.

Figure 4.1: The layers of culture

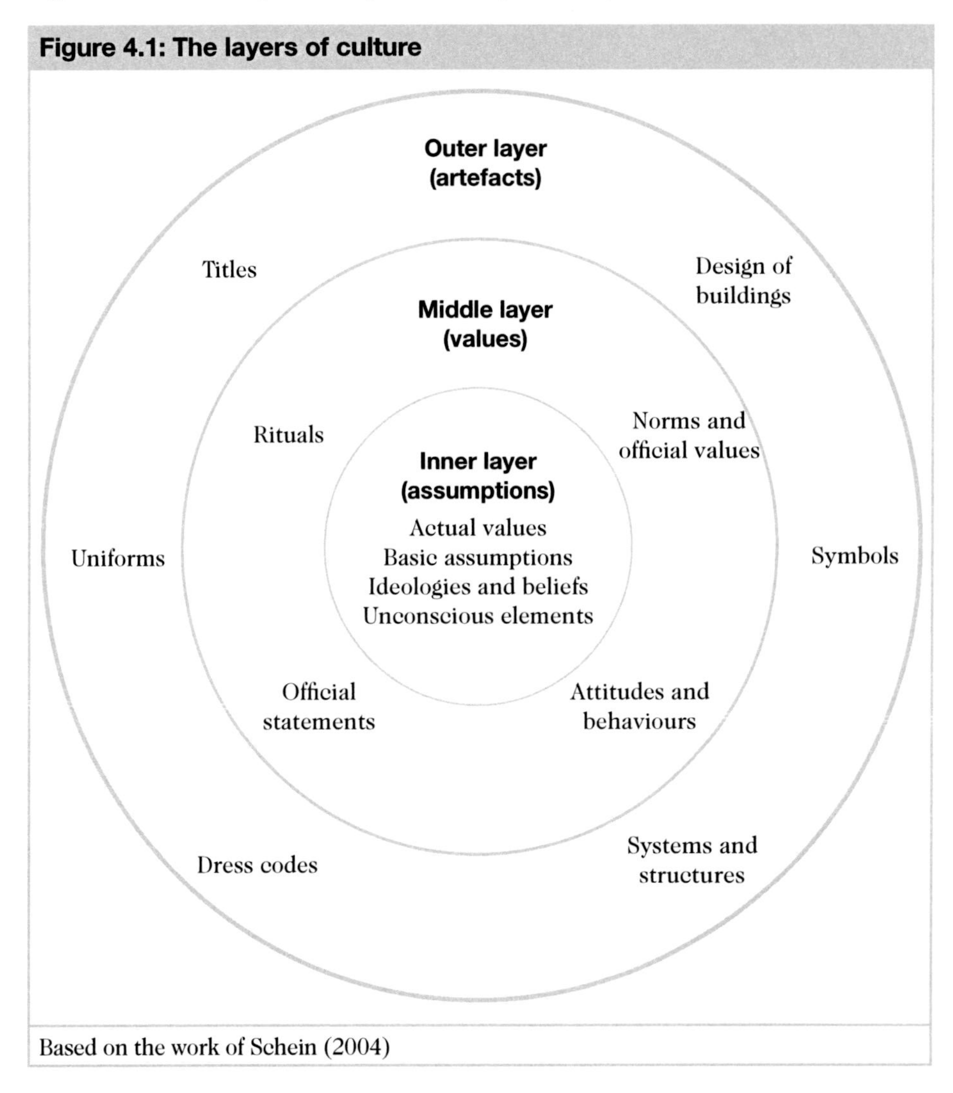

Based on the work of Schein (2004)

If problems are identified by managers, staff or other stakeholders, and providing those attempting to change the organisation have sufficient power and influence and they can convince sufficient colleagues of the value of making changes, it is more likely to be successful. This means that a programme of change can be put in place before the organisation is forced to change as a result of external pressures, with managers and staff recognising that the service is no longer providing appropriate provision and proactively introducing changes to improve the service.

The influence of the paradigm

In this section we dig deeper into the concept of culture and examine how it can influence an organisation. Staff in health and social care services may hold a range of differing beliefs about various aspects of their service, but there is also likely to exist a set of core beliefs and assumptions that are held in common by the majority of staff. This set of common beliefs is described as a 'paradigm' by Johnson and Scholes (2002), and is said to evolve over time and can embrace a range of assumptions, including the nature of the service, its management and the routines which are important to its success. The paradigm of the service is cultural in that it is held commonly by staff, taken for granted and not seen as problematic. Because it is taken for granted it is more easily perceived by those outside a service than those that work within it to whom it is self-evident.

When ways of working are taken for granted, staff may recognise changes that are taking place around them, but this does not necessarily mean that they see such changes as directly relevant to their organisation. If we take the above explanation as a starting point for understanding how culture influences an organisation, we can begin to understand why some organisations continue to provide poor quality service over a long period of time, even though it is receiving signals, both internal and external, that things are changing around it and that its standards are no longer appropriate. The need to change a service is not determined by external forces, but by power of the paradigm, with the information from outside the organisation filtered through the powerful assumptions which represent the 'reality' of the organisation. This also helps us understand how difficult it can be to change an organisation which fails to respond to signals that it needs to change.

Case study

The paradigm: culture within services

In the joint reports of the Commission for Social Care Inspection and the Healthcare Commission (CSCI, 2006/2007) into the Cornwall Partnership Trust, and Merton and Sutton Learning Disability Services, certain features were common to both services and provide an insight into the culture of these services. Both services were poorly led with a lack of strategic vision and inadequate management arrangements. Senior managers failed to recognise that their services were inadequate in spite of recent policy initiatives which described best practice in learning disability services and guidance on protecting vulnerable adults (*Valuing People*, DH, 2001; *No Secrets*, DH, 2000). Serious abuse had taken place in both services, with inadequate use of adult protection procedures.

Attitudes towards service users were paternalistic and failed to provide opportunities for them to develop greater independence, make choices and become part of their communities. Similarly, both services restricted the activities of service users, creating a model of care that promoted dependency. Alongside these shortcomings, the services had inadequate levels of staffing, with poor levels of staff support and training. Working practices were a legacy of previous organisations with little exposure to other ways of working that could have encouraged improved standards of care. As a result, staff lacked an understanding of best practice and the principles contained in the Valuing People strategy. The poor quality found in these services was reflected in the lack of priority given to people with learning disabilities in the two authorities. In both cases a failure to give adequate attention to these services meant they were marginalised, and as a consequence little attention was given to improving performance. The limitations of both services reveal aspects of the power of cultures that are powerful determinants of practice and make the introduction of change so problematic.

Comment

We can see from the case study of these services that they had a number of similar features which suggests that cultural beliefs and assumptions about people with learning disabilities were deeply rooted in these organisations.

These beliefs may have acted as a form of internalised control that influenced how managers and staff responded to the needs of service users, and that past attempts to improve these services came up against these deeply held beliefs to the detriment of service users' needs. What appeared to be missing in these services was visionary leadership that actively developed and communicated ways of working with people with learning difficulties that would have begun to influence and change attitudes. Without an active approach to culture change, alongside a range of other management actions to root out poor practice and a significant investment in education and the training of staff, the power of the existing culture and defences against change would be difficult to overcome.

The cultural web

One way of making sense of organisational culture is to use the concept of the cultural web to represent the 'taken for granted' assumptions or paradigm of an organisation and the physical manifestations of organisational culture developed by Johnson and Scholes (2002). The cultural web can be used to understand an organisation's culture through its rituals, routines, stories, structures and systems (see Figure 4.2 on p.67). Observing these aspects of its culture will enable you to begin to understand the clues to the 'taken for granted' assumptions or paradigm of the organisation and its influence on all its activities. It can help us understand why, even when new strategies are formulated to improve a service, achieving change can be difficult. The elements of culture that make up the web are as follows.

- **Rituals** are the special events through which the organisation emphasises what is important and reinforces 'the way we do things around here', and signals what is especially valued.
- **Routines** are the way members of the organisation behave towards each other, and towards those outside the organisation, and lubricate the workings of a service and may be beneficial, but because they represent a 'taken for granted' approach to practice it can be difficult to change.
- **Stories** told by members of the organisation to each other, outsiders and new recruits, embed the organisational history and flag up important events and personalities, and also highlight mavericks that deviate from the norm.
- **Symbolic aspects** such as logos, offices, titles, and the language and terminology used, particularly in regard to service users.

- **Control systems** used to measure and reward what is important and focus attention and activity, and can be used to shape the behaviour of staff and service users.
- **Power structures** associated with the most powerful people in the organisation and what is actually valued, and closely associated with a core set of assumptions and beliefs.
- **Organisational structures** both formal hierarchical structures and informal ways which reflect the power structure, define important relationships and emphasise what is important in the organisation, and influence working practices, constraints and norms that exercise control over individuals.

All these ingredients of the cultural web protect the paradigm which sits at the centre of the web and powerfully influences how people behave in organisations. Some of this can be recognised from the evidence of the CSCI inspections of the Cornwall and Sutton and Merton services where poor and abusive practices were deeply embedded in the organisations and taken for granted, and demonstrated how several elements of the cultural web reinforced the dysfunctional systems and processes, making the potential for change more difficult.

The cultural web has a number of useful purposes according to Johnson (2001), including:

- revealing what is taken for granted in the organisation by questioning what is not normally questioned. If no one questions what is taken for granted, then change will be more difficult
- mapping the organisational culture can reveal where barriers to change may exist
- revealing the linkages between different aspects of the organisational culture which are particularly resistant to change
- mapping the culture can provide the basis for exploring what changes are needed to deliver a new strategy
- being used to consider whether the proposed strategy can be managed, with practical ways for implementing strategic change developed.

Figure 4.2: The cultural web of the NHS

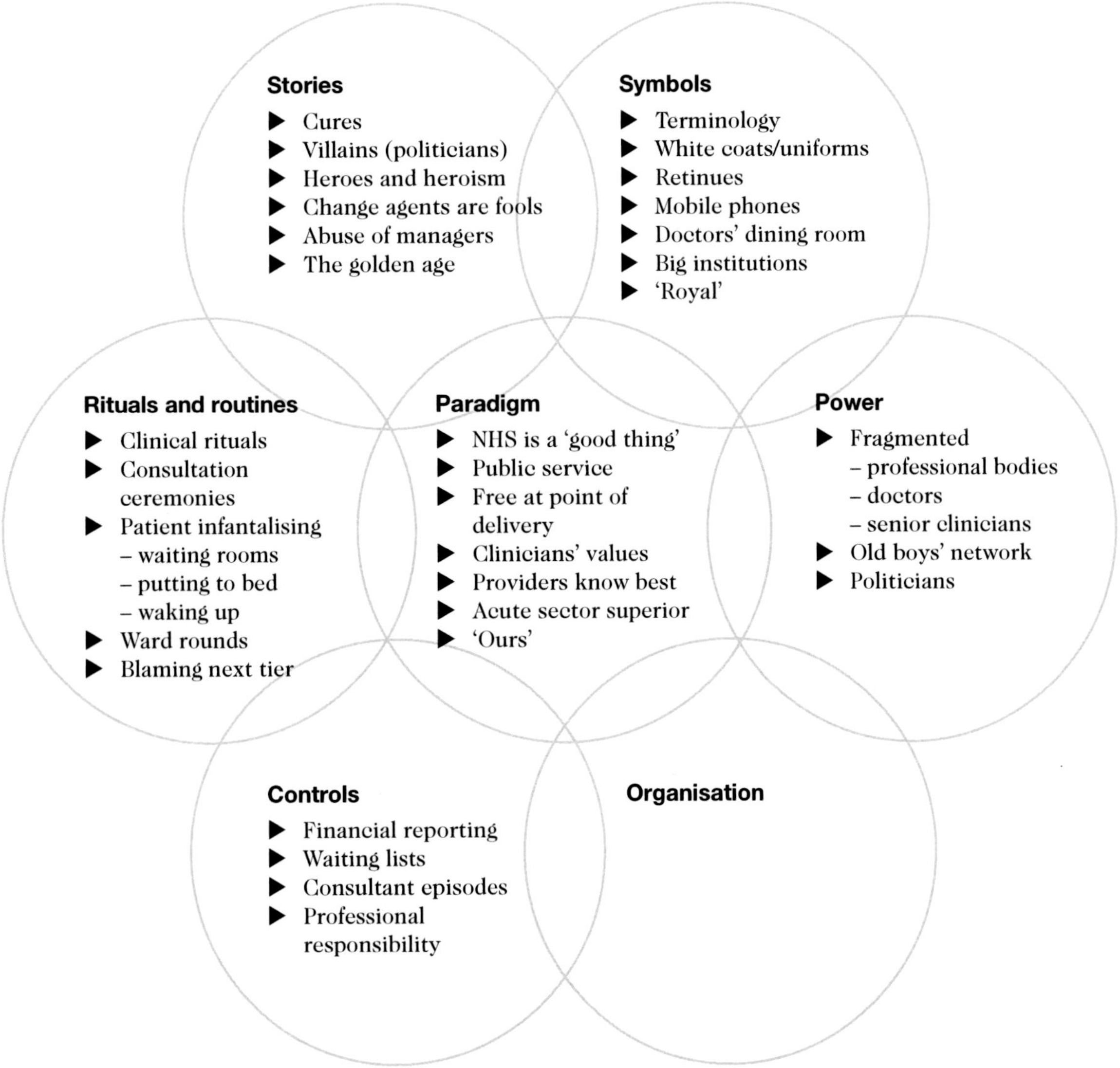

Stories
- Cures
- Villains (politicians)
- Heroes and heroism
- Change agents are fools
- Abuse of managers
- The golden age

Symbols
- Terminology
- White coats/uniforms
- Retinues
- Mobile phones
- Doctors' dining room
- Big institutions
- 'Royal'

Rituals and routines
- Clinical rituals
- Consultation ceremonies
- Patient infantalising
  - waiting rooms
  - putting to bed
  - waking up
- Ward rounds
- Blaming next tier

Paradigm
- NHS is a 'good thing'
- Public service
- Free at point of delivery
- Clinicians' values
- Providers know best
- Acute sector superior
- 'Ours'

Power
- Fragmented
  - professional bodies
  - doctors
  - senior clinicians
- Old boys' network
- Politicians

Controls
- Financial reporting
- Waiting lists
- Consultant episodes
- Professional responsibility

Organisation

This diagram of a cultural web represents the taken for granted aspects of the NHS in the 1990s

Reproduced with permission from *Exploring Corporate Strategy: Text and cases* (5th edition) © Johnson G & Scholes K (2002) Pearson Education.

Mapping the organisation, using the cultural web, can have other useful benefits when strategic change is proposed. Senior managers often see strategy as something that happens at the top of the organisation which they control. Using the cultural web to map the organisation can reveal those mundane aspects that are important in successfully implementing strategy. It is particularly useful to senior managers to have to recognise that changing the strategy of an organisation will require changes to routines and procedures that are far removed from the vision at the top of the organisation. Just focusing on changing structures without understanding how staff have to implement the strategy on a day-to-day basis can be insufficient to achieve effective implementation. Yet it is the reality of implementing new routines and procedures that will ultimately be the test of effective change. By revealing the cultural complexity of the organisation, through mapping its different elements and identifying the desirable structures, systems and processes that would support a new strategy, can offer pointers to what is important to change (Johnson, 2001).

Culture and socialisation

One of the difficulties facing staff who join an organisation where there is a deeply embedded and dominant culture is that it strongly influences how they behave. When staff are newly appointed they observe how managers and staff conduct themselves and adjust their behaviour accordingly, and are encouraged to conform to ways that are acceptable to the workgroup. Through this process, staff learn new ways of working as the culture is learned, shared and transmitted. This is particularly so in the informal and invisible organisation below the surface, which through the power of the grapevine, informal leadership, needs and relationships have a powerful influence on how new staff respond to demands made on them (Hafford-Letchfield, 2006).

Socialisation in this way results in compliance and conformity to the values, beliefs, attitudes, rules and patterns of the behaviour required, and the way a service works becomes embedded in their unconscious behaviour patterns (Pettinger, 2000). We have seen from the CSCI reports that both services (see case study) investigated had a poor record on staffing, with shortages of staff, reliance on temporary staff, and importantly a low investment in training that could have transmitted positive attitudes with emphasis on best practice, promoting positive messages about individuals, and supporting and empowering individuals to have a voice which is listened to, and acted upon (Williams, 2006). Training alone would not necessarily change an organisation's culture, but it could act as an opposing force along with other more strategic initiatives.

Even in services where there is a history of more effective working practices, attempting to introduce new ways of working may challenge deeply embedded subcultures, confronting the belief that 'the way we've always done things works best'. Although staff may not make explicit statements to this effect, their practices may continue as before, in spite of management statements about improvements in the service. This is often described as the 'rhetoric and reality of change', where new initiatives and innovations come up against resistance, informed by what is taken for granted in day-to-day practice.

Introducing change can be particularly difficult where the existing culture is strongly embedded as a result of years of practices that have reinforced particular forms of working, especially if they are supported by management decisions and powerful individuals whose actions and statements shape the behaviour of junior or newly appointed staff. The culture may be so powerful that staff who are unhappy with current practices are inhibited from raising matters about poor performance for fear of ostracism or bullying. Whistle-blowing in such situations becomes extremely difficult because there is no confidence that senior managers will recognise, let alone respond to, exposure of abusive cultures. Similarly, complaints by service users and their carers can often be disregarded as they are in a weak position in terms of power in the organisational structure and their views can be ignored where they challenge the dominant belief system.

The starting point for any attempt to change the culture of a service needs to be rooted in the underpinning of values that constitute the basis for a high quality service that engages with service users and carers and explores how a service can be provided from their perspective. Without a strong and coherent vision of the sort of service they want to provide, those leading a service will find it more difficult to engage with staff, service users and carers in developing a set of shared principles about good practice. It is in relation to a vision for services that the concept of social role valorisation developed in work with people with learning difficulties. This concept offers a vision that is particularly important as it can help challenge negative perceptions of people at risk of social exclusion (Cocks, 2001). The associated service evaluation model PASSING (Williams, 2006) is valuable in requiring learners to experience services from the service user's perspective. This can change attitudes of staff even when their managers are unwilling to embrace change.

We have seen in the examples of services investigated that there was poor quality management at different levels in the service. Management problems were compounded by a lack of strategic vision about the future of the services which was not guided by the *Valuing People* policy (DH, 2001). Nor was there an understanding and willingness to use adult protection policies and procedures to safeguard service users (Cambridge, 2007). Managers have a key leadership role in change, both in terms of setting out a direction for the service and motivating staff to strive to reach new goals, but also in sponsoring and legitimising the change process on a day-to-day basis (Gilbert, 2005). Leaders can create the conditions that enable others to change their practice.

Improving practice

Change can take a range of forms and is related to the extent to which a service is able to modify its activities, for example, to enable it to develop up-to-date policies and procedures. If a service is managed proactively, is responsive to its external environment and anticipates the need for change, progress can be achieved through a proactive process of incremental change, where over time the service gradually adapts to new ways of working, drawing on models of best practice. This form of evolutionary change is rooted in continually analysing the need for change and using change models to improve the performance of the service. This has much in common with the concept of learning organisations (Gould & Baldwin, 2004), which continually adjust their strategies as the environment around them changes. Such incremental change was lacking in the examples of abusive regimes, with inward looking, isolated services having failed to change incrementally until exposed through the media or external inspection.

Where managers fail to see the need for major changes, but adapt the current ways of operating within the existing paradigm, it can eventually result in a crisis when the organisation's future is at risk. Failing to change sufficiently to fundamentally improve the organisation can lead to strong external pressure that may result in transformational change which challenges the existing paradigm and means the imposition of change to the 'taken for granted' assumptions and 'the way we do things around here' (Johnson & Scholes, 2002). Such change usually comes about as a result of both reactive and proactive processes. For example, if there is a significant deterioration in performance or strong external criticism which threatens the future of the service, then the management may find itself in a forced transformational change situation where the existing paradigm and service routines can no longer meet the new requirements. As happened in the Cornwall and Sutton and Merton Trusts, this is likely to be disruptive and painful with significant consequences for those who manage and staff the service.

Long-standing managers are often trapped in the same paradigm as other staff and less aware of the signals that suggest radical change is needed. Radical change of a transformational nature often follows the appointment of a new senior manager with a remit to introduce change, in the face of a crisis or rapidly deteriorating performance. In the reports of the Cornwall and Sutton and Merton Trusts we saw that change had been attempted in the past, but these changes had not had a significant impact on these services, and were peripheral to the main problems and insufficient to deal with the poor conditions and practices that led to abuse. Any changes that were made appeared to be bounded within the existing paradigm in the services, when more radical levels of change were needed to transform these services. Ultimately, the intervention of an external agency resulted in forced change that challenged the existing paradigm and began the transformation process.

Although organisational cultures that are deeply embedded are seen as difficult to change, Schein (2004) argues that a culture can be influenced by the things that leaders pay attention to. This perspective on change suggests that what leaders systematically work on and communicate to others sends out signals to the rest of the organisation about issues that are considered to be important. For example, if the leader is someone who engages with staff, communicates the importance of good practice and works to create a culture of openness and trust, this will send out signals about what is valued, which in time will begin to change the organisation. At the practice level, leadership on the part of frontline managers is also important, as they support, monitor and develop practice and are the bridge between senior management and frontline staff (Scragg, 2009). A part of their role is to interpret organisational strategies in terms of day-to-day practice, and at the same time act as an anchor and guide for staff at times of change. They also have a particularly important role in promoting and sustaining practice standards through support for individual practitioners and teams in their supervisory and consultative responsibilities (Kearney, 2004). It is also important to stress that first line managers tend to be trusted more than senior managers, adding credibility when communicating and explaining the need for changes to practice (Larkin & Larkin, 1996).

Summary

This chapter has introduced the concept of organisational culture and its influence on how a service is provided. The first section has revealed the range and complexity of factors that support an organisation's culture and why it can be resistant to change. We have seen how deeply held basic assumptions make change and innovation difficult in services and why successive change initiatives can fail. In the second section, the pervasive influence of culture on organisations is discussed, highlighted by the case study which demonstrates the power of cultural factors, and where staff with a lack of appropriate leadership, training and support, carry attitudes into their work that can reinforce patterns of abuse. Finally, the chapter has described some of the management processes that are involved in changing a service, and the complex and challenging agenda involved in transforming services where powerful cultures have developed over many years and can be resistant to change.

References

Cambridge P (2007) In safe hands, protecting people with learning disabilities from abuse. In: S Carnaby (Ed) *Learning Disability Today*. Brighton: Pavilion.

Cocks E (2001) Normalisation and social role valorisation: guidance for human services development. *Hong Kong Journal of Psychiatry* **1** (1) 12–16.

Commission for Social Care Inspection (2006) *Joint Investigation into the Provision of Services for People with Learning Disabilities at Cornwall Partnership NHS Trust.* London: CSCI. (www.cqc.org.uk)

Commission for Social Care Inspection (2007) *Joint Investigation into the Service for People with Learning Disabilities Provided by Sutton and Merton Primary Care Trust.* London: CSCI. (www.cqc.org.uk)

Department of Health (2000) *No Secrets: Guidance on developing and implementing multi-agency protection for vulnerable adults*. London: The Stationery Office.

Department of Health (2001) *Valuing People: A new strategy for learning disability in the 21st century*. London: The Stationery Office.

Gilbert P (2005) *Leadership: Being effective and remaining human*. Lyme Regis: Russell House Publishing.

Gould N & Baldwin M (2004) *Social Work, Critical Reflection and the Learning Organization*. Aldershot: Ashgate.

Hafford-Letchfield T (2006) *Management and Organisations in Social Work*. Exeter: Learning Matters.

Harrison R & Stokes H (1992) *Diagnosing Organizational Culture (Transforming Social Work Practice)*. London: Pfieffer and Company.

Johnson G (2001) Mapping and re-mapping organisational culture: a local government example. In: G Johnson & J Scholes (Eds) *Exploring Public Sector Strategy*. Harlow: Pearson Education.

Johnson G & Scholes K (2002) *Exploring Corporate Strategy: Text and cases* (6th edition). Harlow: Pearson Education.

Kearney P (2004) First line managers: the mediators of standards and quality of practice. In: D Statham (Ed) *Managing Front Line Practice in Social Care*. London: Jessica Kingsley.

Larkin TJ & Larkin S (1996) Reaching and changing frontline employees. *Harvard Business Review*, June, 95–104.

McAuley J & Shanahan P (1994) *Managing Your Organisation*. Buckingham: Open University.

Meyerson D & Martin J (1987) Cultural change: an integration of three different views. *Journal of Management Studies* **24** (6) 623–647.

Ogbonna E (1993) Managing organisational culture: fantasy or reality? *Human Resources Management Journal* **3** (2) 42–55.

Pettinger R (2000) *Mastering Organisational Behaviour*. Basingstoke: Palgrave Macmillan.

Schein E (2004) *Organizational Culture and Leadership* (3rd edition) San Francisco: Jossey-Bass.

Scragg T (2006) An evaluation of integrated team management. *Journal of Integrated Care* **14** (3) 39–48.

Scragg T (2009) *Managing at the Front Line: A handbook for managers in social care services*. Brighton: Pavilion Publishing.

Williams P (2006) *Social Work with People with Learning Disability*. Exeter: Learning Matters.

Section 2:

People central to change

Chapter 5

Leadership roles in change

Key points

- Effective leaders have a range of attributes, particularly related to personal qualities
- Leadership can be transformational or transactional, or combine elements of both roles
- Perceptions of leadership are changing as more individuals play a role in change, with a wide range of roles in the implementation process
- Leaders who work collectively strengthen the change process
- Understanding the importance of communication and political dimensions of change are essential

Introduction

In the space of a few years the style of management in health and social care organisations has had to change to encompass many more aspects of leadership as services move from conditions of relative stability to those of constant change. This chapter will explore what is meant by leadership, the essential qualities leaders need to demonstrate, the different forms that leadership can take, and the range of leadership roles in managing change. It recognises that leadership can be found throughout organisations; whether it is those at the top of the organisation where leaders are responsible for formulating strategy, or frontline managers who lead change at the operational level.

What constitutes leadership?

Brown (1996) described leadership as the interaction and shared communication about the direction of a service, the need for change and improving service delivery between those who have positional power and authority to respond to the need for change and those who have to implement change at the frontline of services. This functional view can be underpinned by a small number of essential qualities that we recognise in those who are described as leaders. Gilbert (2005) describes them as follows.

- **Integrity, authenticity and trust**. The leader is someone who is trustworthy and who others can trust. Not only a leader who says the right thing, but acts on their beliefs ('walks the talk'). Staff can feel they are working with someone they believe is honest and has character and conviction. Leaders need to demonstrate the desired mindset and behaviours at all times and act as role models. Their activities and statements are amplified throughout an organisation. If leaders appear to be paying lip service to change then this sends a signal across the organisation that commitment to change is limited.
- **Values**. The leader has explicit values which link with personal integrity. This could also be described as a mode of conduct that is socially preferable, for example, attitudes towards people with special needs that set an example to others.
- **Providing direction or vision**. This is about providing staff with a picture of a desired future state, which needs to be better in some ways than the current situation, or where it is important to avoid the current situation getting worse. Much of this is about the sustained personal commitment of the leader who can communicate a clear vision of the future firmly based on strong values.
- **Inspiration and empowerment**. This is about engaging with individuals' hearts and minds so that they feel committed to moving forward to achieve a desired future. Importantly it is also about empowering staff to work on change without constantly having to check with the leader. This emphasises the dangers of micro-management which undermines confidence and commitment.
- **Delivery**. The test of a leader is how far they actually deliver what they set out to do. Leaders are judged on their performance and how effective and supporting they are at creating coalitions that can implement strategies which move the organisation forward. To achieve change requires persistence, and leaders who are successful are likely to be those who have direct experience of practice and know what needs to be done to effectively implement change.

These aspects of leadership chime with the personal qualities and values identified in the *NHS Leadership Qualities Framework* (2006) where the complexity of change and the personal accountability of leaders demands a series of personal qualities, including:

- **self-belief:** outstanding leaders are positive and have a sense of confidence which enables the leader to shape rather than follow; this includes relishing a challenge, being prepared to stand up for what you believe in, working beyond the call of duty when required and speaking out when this is needed
- **self-awareness:** outstanding leaders have a high degree of self-awareness and they know their own strengths and limitations, with failure or misjudgement used as an opportunity for learning; this includes being aware of one's own emotions and your personal impact on others, particularly when they are under pressure
- **self-management:** outstanding leaders are able to pace themselves and are persistent; this includes being tenacious and resilient in the face of difficulty, and being able to cope with an increasingly complex environment
- **personal integrity:** outstanding leaders bring a sense of integrity to what they do; this includes believing in a set of key values and a commitment to the service, insistence on openness and communication, acting as a role model and the ability to press for change in the interests of developing or improving the service.

Another way of looking at leadership draws on the work of Hartley and Allison (2000). They describe three perspectives. The first focuses on a range of personal characteristics, behaviours, skills and style of the leader as a person (the 'who') and how they shape events and circumstances. The individual who is able to achieve this can bring about the transformation of an organisation. The weakness in this perspective is that it can overemphasise the power of the individual and ignore the roles of others in an organisation who each play a critical role in change.

Second, there is the position perspective, which is often related to the leader's place in the hierarchy of an organisation, such as a chief executive or director. Although these formal positions give the person authority, they do not guarantee leadership, which is more than simply holding office. In contrast, a person who has no formal position may still be a leader if others regard them as influential.

Third, there are the processes (the 'how') that occur between individuals, groups and organisations, that are concerned with motivating and influencing people, and shaping and achieving outcomes. This perspective places less emphasis on the notion of the exceptional person and their ability to overcome problems, but more on the ability to work with other people and influence them to find workable solutions to problems where there may be no easy solutions.

In addition to these perspectives, Rogers and Reynolds (2003) add a fourth, which is concerned with purpose (the 'why'). This provides the reason for doing something and is related to the underpinning values of an organisation. They describe the purpose as setting a vision and determining strategy that connects with the primary task of the organisation. They also recognise that increasingly the purpose can go beyond any one organisation through the collaborative work between different agencies. Together these four aspects link the leader to the 'who', 'how' and 'why' of change.

The attributes of effective leaders: social care workers' views

When a group of social care workers were asked to describe managers they worked with who demonstrated leadership qualities, they suggested the following attributes marked out those with leadership qualities (Scragg, 2009):

- 'a clear vision of where the team is going'
- 'a good communicator'
- 'an ideas person'
- 'enthusiastic and motivated'
- 'approachable and a good listener'
- 'works alongside people and acknowledges their contribution'
- 'doesn't take the credit for others' work or ideas'
- 'supportive and takes an interest in team members'
- 'values team members' contributions and shows it'
- 'delegates work and trusts colleagues to take decisions'.

Some of these attributes could be considered to be qualities found in any effective manager, whereas the social care workers emphasised vision, suggesting ideas and being an enthusiastic communicator, as things that set some managers apart and suggested they also had leadership qualities. These confirm Gilbert's (2005) view that effective leadership centres around a small number of personal qualities which are recognised and valued by staff. He also identifies areas of management that require a transactional approach, for example, creating services and systems, but the growing demands on services and their managers suggest the need for a much more dynamic process that creates a positive culture and takes services forward.

Transformational leadership

From these descriptions emerges a much clearer picture of what constitutes leadership and can be seen to focus on a group of personal qualities, and their formal position in an organisation, as well as their personal style and ways of working with others. Many of these responsibilities and personal qualities can be found in Burns' (1978) description of the 'transformational' leader who involves their staff in transforming themselves and the way they work. Emphasis is on inspiring staff around shared values and developing a purposeful approach to the development of the service.

This is increasingly common currency in many public services, with its emphasis on creating the conditions for commitment to fundamental change in services based on vision and innovation. In this role we see the leader creating a long-term vision for the organisation, setting the broad purpose and direction, and motivating and inspiring staff by satisfying the need for achievement, recognition and self-esteem. Leadership is therefore concerned with developing more effective systems and looking to the future and the creation of significant change.

Case study

Transformational leadership

A third sector organisation providing traditional services for people with learning disabilities had recently appointed a new chief executive. She was alert to changes in the external environment of the service and provided an opportunity to reshape the existing services and improve the quality of lives of people using them. The CEO, who had extensive experience of learning disability services and a deep personal commitment to personalised services, recognised that there were service users living in residential homes who, with limited support, could live more independently. To take advantage of the new funding stream she formed a strategic partnership with a housing association following the announcement of the *Supporting People* initiative, which made it possible to financially support those service users who wished to live in their own homes. The CEO argued convincingly that the formation of the partnership with the housing association would be in the longer-term interests of the organisation, although this would mean giving up ownership of a range of properties that were closely identified with the original foundation of the service. This would also allow the organisation to focus on its core strengths of person-centred care, rather than property management.

Following approval of this decision, a number of older residential homes were refurbished to provide individual accommodation. In addition, new accommodation was provided, enabling 21 service users to move into their own apartments. This initiative took the organisation in a new direction strategically as it demonstrated that most service users, with the appropriate support, could live more independently in the community. The organisation gradually reduced its dependence on traditional residential accommodation, which in turn led to the development of expanded staff roles, working methods and job satisfaction. The development also provided a more diverse range of accommodation for service users, who in turn also expressed greater satisfaction with the service. The CEO's initiative subsequently led to the development of further partnerships with a wide range of housing providers and significantly expanded the service and its reputation.

Comment

The case example demonstrates the importance of senior managers being sensitive to changes in the external environment and that if capitalised on they can be used as drivers for change. The CEO had kept abreast of policy initiatives and was quick to respond to a change in policy that could benefit the organisation. She used her leadership skills to develop a strategic alliance with another organisation to fundamentally transform the service and improve the lives of service users. This change resulted in a traditional organisation becoming much more outward-looking and responsive to change, which made it easier to develop subsequent partnerships.

Transactional leadership

Burns (1978) also described a form of leadership that we recognise as management. Here leadership focuses on achieving current objectives, resolving day-to-day problems and ensuring that staff meet their contractual obligations. These activities can be termed as 'transactional' in that they describe the relationship between manager and staff, with the emphasis on agreement about organisational goals and objectives; the work to be undertaken and outcomes required. The focus is on the present and ensuring that services are delivered effectively and efficiently in accordance with an organisation's policies and procedures. These are the essential processes to ensure that routine work is carried out. From this description we can see that transactional management is concerned with planning, organising, implementing and controlling. They are the main functions of management based on a 'contract' with mutual expectations on the part of the manager and member of staff. It is a contract that requires acceptance of managerial authority, although this will differ depending on the professional status and skills of the individual members of staff.

Integration of leadership and management roles

This description of transactional leadership is increasingly questioned as health and social care services demand that managers provide direction and inspiration in a continually changing workplace environment. This means extending the concept of management to encompass the attributes found in transformational leaders. Frontline managers are also increasingly drawn into more strategic activity through work with senior managers on service development and with other agencies where service partnerships are developing or working together on change. The more recent view of management and leadership acknowledges this reality and that there is considerable overlap between the two roles and it is increasingly recognised that they are integrated and complementary rather than separate. The complementary nature of leadership and management is recognised in the Skills for Care (2006) report identifying what this means for social care services. They see leadership and management as integrated, so that leadership is reflected in management roles at all levels. In this view leadership and management are seen as a continuum, with the view that most leaders also need management skills and most managers are more effective if they are able to develop leadership behaviours and skills. The complementary nature of leadership and management is described in Figure 5.1, on p.84, which illustrates the activities of leaders and managers, and also elements that are common to both roles.

Figure 5.1: The relationship between leadership and management

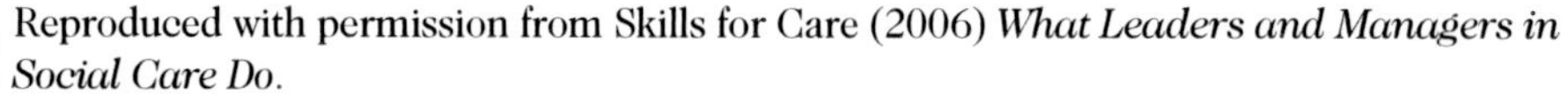
Reproduced with permission from Skills for Care (2006) *What Leaders and Managers in Social Care Do*.

What we are seeing, with increasing emphasis on leadership, is the recognition that management is moving away from getting results by close control of the workforce and towards a more enabling and empowering relationship (Mullins, 2007). This could also be described as a shift from the traditional command and control model of management to one that reflects the sorts of activities found in organisations which value constant improvement and transformation.

It can be difficult to combine the attributes of management and leadership in the same person, although this is an ideal (Gilbert, 2005). Gilbert argues that to drive change forward leaders need to break away from the day-to-day cycle of organising and controlling (traditional management) and focus on listening, empowering and inspiring people. He believes leaders need to stand back and fix their eyes on the horizon, while at the same time being in touch with the views of those they serve. In this view, leadership is twinned with management so that the leader is both strategic in their vision, but also attentive to the day-to-day demands on the service. This view is reinforced by Peters and Waterman (1995) who describe effective leadership as both value-shaping at one level and concerned with implementation at another. They portray this as mastery of two ends of the spectrum with the leader giving their attention to ideas and also attention to detail.

Changing perceptions of leadership

We have seen that leadership is an evolving concept in health and social care services driven largely by the need for radical change in organisations. This has in turn led to the development of concepts of leadership that take us beyond the established ideas based on transactional and transformational approaches and explores other models.

Leadership no longer stops with managers. Rapidly changing health and social care environments, technologies that result in greater information dissemination and exchange, more inter-organisational relationships and networking and greater empowerment of staff, means that many more team members are involved in decision-making and strategic activities today than in the past (Fulop *et al*, 2004).

These developments accord with the idea of drawing on the talents and commitment of all team members and lead naturally to the concept of distributed or devolved leadership, where leadership is distributed and encouraged among a wide range of staff. Leadership is not about position alone, but willingness and responsibility for all members of a team to lead. It reinforces the view that it is not only managers who can be leaders, but leadership should be encouraged from others as it is important at all levels of an organisation (Rogers & Reynolds, 2003). As confidence in the leadership role grows, it is important to empower staff and encourage those with flair who can take the service forward. This also demonstrates the importance of the relationship between leadership and influence. Although leadership is associated with position, and usually means the person at the top of the organisation, in fact leadership can exist at any level in an organisation where there are individuals who have influence.

Leadership roles in change

In his guide to strategic planning in the public sector, Bryson (2004) describes a series of important tasks that leaders, in different roles in an organisation, need to give attention to if the planning and implementation of change is to be effective.

Understanding the context

Leaders need to have an appreciation of the external and internal context that will influence decisions about change. This requires a detailed knowledge of the organisation alongside the use of techniques such as environmental assessments, cultural mapping, stakeholder analysis, and assessment of strengths and weaknesses. A detailed understanding of the context can help in making decisions about what processes to use to improve the organisation (see Chapter 3). Crucial decisions will need to be made about the scale of change and what forces are acting on the organisation which demand a response. This may mean a major shift in the organisational strategy that transforms the organisation's structures, systems and processes, or is more incremental and part of an ongoing programme of continual improvement.

Understanding yourself and other people involved

Leading change is demanding work and requires determination and tenacity. Strategic change by its very nature impacts on the lives of others and is likely to result in challenge and resistance. Understanding your own strengths and limitations is essential as crafting and guiding strategic change will test the most resilient leader (NHS Leadership Qualities Framework, 2006). This is where Gilbert's (2005) essential aspects of leadership play an important role in anchoring change in the values and vision for the organisation that will lead to a better future.

Understanding oneself is helped by the concept of 'emotional intelligence' (Goleman, 1996). This concept is essential about the self, which encompasses the capacity to recognise one's own feelings and those of others, and for managing one's own emotions. It focuses on how leaders handle themselves and their relationships with colleagues to good effect. It is about all those elements that go to make up the individual who is a leader and in who, without having self-knowledge, the skills of leadership would be ineffective. In working with others, leaders need to develop their skills in managing relationships and need to understand their own emotions, and be able to manage them and recognise them in others. To be effective, leaders need to be prepared to learn about themselves and be willing to make necessary changes, although it is recognised how demanding this personal learning can be (Hill, 2003). Many of the elements that make up the components of emotional intelligence echo the sort of attributes staff in health and social care services seek in those who lead their service, which combine the effective management skills with the well developed people skills found in effective leaders.

Sponsoring change

Senior managers who initiate strategic change processes may not be involved subsequently in the day-to-day work of implementation, but they nevertheless play an important role in sponsoring change. By the nature of their role they have the power and authority to commit the organisation to strategic change and hold people accountable to maintain progress. It is their responsibility to communicate the reasons for change and what change is intended to achieve, particularly where there is scepticism about the need for change. Articulating the need for change could include describing the results of environmental assessments undertaken and significant changes that threaten the organisation and the imperatives for change. Engaging in a dialogue with those affected by change is crucial in anticipating where conflicts and blockages may occur. This also provides an opportunity to encourage ideas from whatever quarter that can contribute to more effective implementation.

Change champions, facilitators and consultants

In small organisations the sponsor and champion can be one and the same person, but usually the champion is someone who is crucial in managing the day-to-day processes of implementing change. They can also be described as change agents. What they have in common is a commitment to the process of change and are comfortable working across organisational boundaries, bringing people together, freeing up resources and doing all the mundane detailed work necessary to keep the process from stalling. They are responsible for keeping the change at the forefront of people's agendas, tracking progress and attending to concerns about implementation. Other important roles include internal or external consultants who can help design the implementation process at an early stage of the change, or facilitate groups of staff who are working on implementation. What these people should bring is skills in working with groups where they can support staff who are learning to work through problems of implementation.

Because people working at the front line are dealing with day-to-day tasks, it is all too easy for new practices to be sidelined. This is where change champions and others in facilitation roles have an important part to play in ensuring that staff introducing new ways of working are supported and deal with the inevitable tensions that arise when people are asked to work in new ways. A significant part of the work of change champions and team leaders is to maintain commitment, interest and enthusiasm.

The importance of collective leadership and a broad coalition

Successful strategic change is the result of collective achievement. A wide range of people are essential to successfully implement change as no one person can have sufficient information for this to be achieved single-handedly. This highlights one of the dangers of the over-reliance on the charismatic leader where change can falter if attention is shifted to other agendas or that person moves on. We have seen in Chapter 3 that Pettigrew *et al*'s (1992) research on strategic change demonstrated that change had a greater chance of success if there was a broad coalition of managers and professionals involved in leading the process, rather than relying on one person to drive change. This means that leaders need to know and trust those who will be involved in the planning and implementation of change. This will also mean investing in people to ensure that they have the skills and knowledge to carry out the tasks that contribute to the achievement of the strategy.

Building an effective coalition is a key part of strategic change. With insufficient people at different levels in the organisation who constitute the team that will lead change, then change is always vulnerable. Once a strategic plan for change is established, implementation relies significantly on frontline managers and other staff. We have seen in earlier chapters that change is likely to fail at the implementation stage when insufficient work has been done communicating and resourcing managers and staff at the front line who have to make new strategies work in practice.

Bryson (2004) argues that the creation of networks and building coalitions is premised on the idea that people can achieve more together than separately. To ensure that networks and coalitions support change, the leaders need to articulate their vision of an improved organisation that supports the strategies for change. This means engaging with a wide range of stakeholders with the message tailored to the particular interests of different stakeholder groups. By building coalitions with both mutual and diverse interests, there is greater likelihood that contentious issues will be resolved and greater ownership of change generated. Although it is unlikely that all interests can be accommodated when new ways of working are proposed, successful coalitions can foster greater democratic relations between those who lead change and those who follow.

Communicating the need for change

Communication is central to effective change. Unless leaders are able to engage with others to communicate their optimism and vision of the future, it is unlikely they will genuinely persuade people to change. It is the ability to motivate and encourage others to believe in themselves, and in turn their ability to lead change that builds confidence and ownership of change. Johnson and Scholes (2002) suggest that leaders typically significantly underestimate the extent to which people understand the need for change. They emphasise that strategic change can be complex and this needs to be communicated across the organisation in a way that gives meaning to the complexity of change. Clarifying and simplifying the priorities of the strategy may also be necessary, with key aspects emphasised rather than expecting to communicate the overall complexity and ramifications. They also suggest that how information is communicated is important, with the correct media chosen. They also stress involving a range of people in the strategy formation which creates greater opportunity for communicating the purpose of change. Feedback should also be encouraged to ensure that changes are discussed by those that have to implement them, and that strategies have a realistic prospect of successful implementation. Leaders can also improve the prospects of change by 'walking the talk' and meeting the staff responsible for implementing change, particularly on an informal basis.

Political aspect of change and challenging established ways of working

One of the important tasks that leaders face when implementing change is to recognise the political aspect of the organisation (Bryson, 2004). Political influences play a significant role in health and social care organisations as elected representatives and multiple stakeholders each play a part in attempting to shape strategic change. Leaders need to be aware of the political influences on the organisation, both the large 'P' and small 'p' issues, and that any proposed change is likely to see an increase in political activity as different interest groups seek advantage in new situations. For leaders implementing change, established rules and procedures, along with entrenched attitudes, can severely constrain change. A willingness to challenge rules when they hinder new ways of working or take calculated risks is an essential part of the leader's commitment to meet change targets and priorities.

Summary

This chapter has examined leadership from a number of perspectives, describing the personal qualities recognised in those leaders who inspire trust and motivation in others. The personal qualities found in individuals who are described as transformational leaders suggests that there is a close relationship between individual personal qualities and the ability to lead successful strategic change. This view of leadership has important implications for those in management roles, who in turn also play a part in strategic implementation. The need for the ownership of change means that leadership is something that needs to be distributed throughout an organisation, not purely the preserve of those in the most senior roles.

This chapter has also described a series of important roles identified by Bryson, in establishing the need for change, building a successful coalition of committed people to lead change, and understanding the importance of communicating and dealing with implementation issues. Underpinning these actions is the recognition of the need for personal awareness of both the self and others. This is critical to the use of the softer skills of people management and is often neglected in those leading change.

References

Brown J (1996) *Chance Favours the Prepared Mind: Leadership, teamwork and mapping change for human resources*. London: HMSO.

Bryson JM (2004) *Strategic Planning for Public and Nonprofit Organizations: A guide to strengthening and sustaining organizational achievement* (3rd edition). San Francisco: Jossey-Bass.

Burns JM (1978) *Leadership*. London: Harper Row.

Fulop L, Linstead S & Dunford R (2004) Leading and managing. In: S Linstead, L Fulop & Lilley S (Eds) *Management and Organization: A critical text*. Basingstoke: Palgrave Macmillan.

Gilbert P (2005) *Leadership: Being effective and remaining human*. Lyme Regis: Russell House Publishing.

Goleman D (1996) *Emotional Intelligence*. London: Bloomsbury.

Hartley J & Allison M (2000) The role of leadership in the modernisation and improvement of public services. In: J Reynolds, J Henderson, J Seden, J Charlesworth & A Bullen (Eds) (2003) *The Managing Care Reader*. Abingdon: Routledge.

Hill LA (2003) *Becoming a Manager: How new managers master the challenges of leadership*. Boston: Harvard Business School Press.

Johnson G & Scholes K (2002) *Exploring Corporate Strategy* (6th edition). Harlow: Pearson Education.

Mullins LJ (2007) *Management and Organisational Behaviour* (8th edition). Harlow: Pearson Education.

NHS (2006) *Leadership Qualities Framework* [online]. Available at: www.nhsleadershipqualities.nhs.uk (accessed June 2010).

Peters T & Waterman RH (1995) *In Search of Excellence: Lessons from America's best-run companies*. London: HarperCollins Business.

Pettigrew A, Ferlie E & McKee L (1992) *Shaping Strategic Change: Making changes in large organisations: The case of the NHS*. London: Sage.

Rogers A & Reynolds J (2003) Leadership and vision. In: J Seden & J Reynolds (Eds) *Managing Care Practice*. London: Routledge and Open University.

Scragg T (2009) *Managing at the Front Line: A handbook for managers in social care* (2nd edition). Brighton: Pavilion.

Skills for Care (2006) *What Leaders and Managers in Social Care Do*. Leeds: Skills for Care (www.skillsforcare.org.uk).

Chapter 6

Human factors in change

Key points

- Importance of positive workplace relations
- The role of the psychological contract in the management of change
- Recognising the stages of transition individuals experience when being asked to change
- Understanding why individuals respond in different ways to change
- Factors that may lead individuals to resist change
- Steps that can be taken to support people during change

Introduction

Making changes to a service will demand that attention is given to a wide range of structural and organisational processes, but probably the most important are the human factors concerned with the responses and reactions of individuals who have to respond to change. Their responses will be largely dependent on their relationships with those leading change, and the arrangements made to support them as they are required to develop new skills or ways of working. How staff who are being asked to change are managed needs to be central to any change proposal and is critical to successful implementation. In this chapter we will focus on what constitutes effective management and the reactions of individuals as they are asked to change, and some of the reasons why change is resisted and the arrangements that need to be put in place to support staff.

Importance of positive workplace relationships

When managers ask staff to respond positively to change and make extra effort to improve the performance of a service it is important that they understand the people they are managing. Understanding people is at the heart of health and social care and is evidenced in positive working relationships and good working conditions (Skye *et al*, 2003). Treating staff well is at the root of good management practice and is particularly important at times of rapid change.

As working in health and social care services can be physically and emotionally demanding, where staff need high levels of energy and commitment, strong supportive relationships on the part of managers is important. Managers play a critical role in creating the conditions where staff feel motivated and experience satisfaction in the workplace. Where staff feel positive about their relationship with their manager they are more likely to have higher levels of job satisfaction, commitment and loyalty, which in turn is associated with high quality performance and willingness to make that extra contribution to a service's success (Hutchinson & Purcell, 2003).

Research undertaken by the Chartered Institute of Personnel and Development (2004) indentified a range of factors that were most frequently reported in job satisfaction surveys. They include:

- having job security
- having job responsibility, and a job that stretches and challenges
- a good working relationship with colleagues
- a considerate manager
- good conditions of service
- fair remuneration
- good working conditions
- freedom to organise own work
- recognition of achievement, particularly feedback from the manager
- opportunities for career advancement.

When examining the implications of these factors it is important to remember that the responses of professionals and those with strong career ambitions are likely to value different things from those individuals who value routine work, do not have a strong career drive and look for greater managerial direction and control. What this tells us is that individuals have complex orientation to their work and the challenge for the manager is to understand individual members of their staff so they can match the demands of the work with the expectations of staff (Fulop & Linstead, 2004). It should also be remembered that an individual's attitude to their work changes over time as their personal circumstances change, which will influence their willingness to develop new skills or take on new challenges. What many of these factors suggest is that change that is poorly thought through is likely to undermine the individual's job satisfaction and make the subsequent implementation of change more difficult.

The psychological contract

The relationship between managers and their staff is central to the successful management of change. As the demands for change increase in health and social care organisations, managers need to understand how the quality of their relationship with individual members of staff can have a significant influence on the potential for change. The psychological contract is defined as 'the perception between two parties, employee and employer, of what their mutual obligations are towards each other' (CIPD, 2005). In contrast to the legal contract of employment, the psychological contract is a set of expectations that are unwritten and often not verbalised about what individuals expect of their organisation. Employer expectations are more frequently expressed through factors such as conditions of employment, adherence to rules and procedures, responsive to management requests and obligations about job performance. Where the contract is not perceived identically by both parties, it is a potential source of conflict. This is particularly so where the set of expectations that an individual expects from the organisation and in turn what the organisation expects from the individual has not been discussed and differences resolved or at least acknowledged.

Traditionally, the employee expectations focus on good working conditions, job security, fair reward, and opportunities for development and career progression. These expectations remain consistent with more recent work by Woodruffe (1999) who identified three areas. First, how employees are rewarded, including pay and conditions that attract and retain good quality staff; second, career advancement and personal development and being part of an organisation that is respected, and third, job satisfaction, including a sense of direction, respect, autonomy and recognition. Employees also increasingly reported wanting a satisfactory balance between their work and personal lives.

The psychological contract and the management of change

Where change is handled badly, this can breach the psychological contract with the frequent introduction of change programmes leading to a high level of cynicism (Pate *et al*, 2000). Other areas seen as breaching the contract by employees was over issues of pay, communications and personal development. Other areas identified in the study included the way that redundancies were handled and the negative signals these sent out to those who stay in the organisation (CIPD, 2005). This study also found that the scale and pace of change influenced how it was received, with large amounts of organisational change shown to have a negative impact on employee attitudes. Frequent change was said to weaken employees' belief that management was in control, knew what it was doing and steering a constant course for an organisation. Further findings from this study found that large scale restructuring and reorganisation tended to harm employee relations and the propensity to seek alternative employment. A further finding was that culture change programmes were seen to have little effect on employee attitudes and behaviour.

Positive approaches to change

Where organisations making changes recognise the importance of the psychological contract, relationships are not necessarily damaged where managers actively negotiate with employees so that they have a good understanding of the organisation, its strategy, market conditions and financial health. With this information employees are more likely to understand the reason for change (Rousseau, 1996). Rousseau identifies four stages in the successful transformation of the psychological contract:

1. challenging the old contract and explaining why change is necessary
2. involving employees and creating transitional structures to manage change
3. helping employees make sense of the new contract
4. getting consistency in the words and actions across the organisation.

This work demonstrates that the psychological contract is not something that is set in stone, and that the employment relationship involves ongoing adjustment of beliefs and commitments on both sides.

The overall message from studies of the psychological contract suggest that it is about securing the involvement of employees and ensuring they are not taken by surprise. Employees are also expected to be treated fairly and feel that they can trust management. When management has to reverse earlier decisions, and this can be inevitable in complex change, this must be acknowledged and time must be taken to explain why it has happened. Where employees believe that management is dishonest or incompetent they are unlikely to give their commitment to change.

Justifying the need for change

To start the change process individuals who will be affected need to experience some discomfort with the current situation, which enables them to recognise why change is necessary. This is where managers need to describe the gap between what is currently not working and the desired future state. It can provide individuals with the understanding they need to make sense of the reasons for change, and should be conducted in the context of psychological safety where individuals feel comfortable experiencing the discomfort of knowing that the service has to change and what they are currently providing needs improvement. It is important that individuals do not feel so guilty that they are psychologically damaged or guilt ridden that they cease to perform effectively.

The change transition

It is important as a manager responsible for leading change that you do not underestimate the impact the proposed changes will have on individuals. Managers rightly put their energy into setting objectives, allocating responsibilities and identifying milestones for implementation with performance targets that can be monitored. Major changes, such as integrating services or re-provisioning institutional care, are something that can be planned in detail, with targets and outcomes monitored. What is less visible and often receives little attention are the psychological changes that take place when individuals have to respond to the change. This has been described as the process of 'transition', which takes place when individuals leave behind the old ways of working and adjust to the new demands and requirements as a result of change. It is often the transition which is resisted rather than the change as the impact on the individual is not understood. As change becomes more pervasive in health and social care organisations, understanding how change impacts on individuals and how they respond to change demands greater understanding of the process of transition. Similar reactions are found in many other significant life transitions and require sensitivity and trust on the part of those leading change based on relationships of transparency and honesty (Gilbert, 2005).

The process of transition is an internal three-phase psychological re-orientation that individuals experience as they come to terms with change.

These stages can be anticipated and need to be planned for by managers and other staff who have leadership roles in change in order that individuals are supported through the stages of transition.

Stage 1: Ending – letting go of the old situation

A critical part of change is the understanding that individuals affected by change will have to work in new ways, developing new skills and attitudes, and fundamentally question practices that the former routines reinforced on a daily basis. This can be particularly painful for the individual who may have invested significantly in developing skills that are no longer required and their current sense of identity.

This can cause strong reactions including denial of the reality of change and fear and uncertainty about the future. The loss of the security of familiar roles and relationships can reduce their effectiveness and willingness to confront the need for change. As individuals adjust to new ways of working it is essential that they feel comfortable relinquishing those old ways of working that are no longer needed. To adapt successfully to change means letting go of the old and building up the knowledge and skills needed for the new role. This stage has been closely related to bereavement and the associated mourning process where individuals may feel shock, anger, denial and helplessness associated with loss that requires sensitive understanding, with support mechanisms put in place. If individuals get stuck in this stage and their feelings of loss are not recognised and given support, it can hinder change.

Stage 2: The neutral zone – between old and new

This is the stage where individuals find themselves between the old ways of working and the future state. It can also be a time when there is considerable confusion and upheaval in structures and systems as the new ways of working are beginning to be implemented. Individuals find themselves presented with new requirements and behaviours with the future still unclear and the additional demands of the former ways of working alongside the need to take on new activities. This stage can mean rapidly learning a new set of skills and can be uncomfortable and accompanied by feelings of loss as individuals realise that they can no longer rely on using many of their old skills. This can affect confidence and create feelings of helplessness, although these feelings can be part of letting go of the past and developing new skills that enable effective performance in the new role. It is during this stage of implementation that individuals can be critical of the proposed change, which is an opportunity to engage in dialogue about ways to improve implementation. Moving through this stage means that the individual has successfully negotiated this transition and is prepared for the new demands placed on them.

Stage 3: A new beginning

If individuals have successfully moved through the earlier stages they are more likely to be committed to change and have begun to identify with the new ways of working. This can be the stage when there is enthusiasm for the new ways and impatience when progress is slow. Attention needs to be paid to supporting this commitment through strong leadership that enables issues arising out of the practicalities of implementation to be discussed as this can result in creative responses to change, recognising the need for additional resources where these are needed and acknowledging the additional workload that change can impose on those affected by change.

Individual responses to change

In all psychological models of change it is important to recognise that there will always be individual responses to change, dependent on a wide range of personal factors that will influence the individual who sees change affecting them. Although the emphasis is rightly placed on concern for those who experience change as threatening, it should also be recognised that some individuals will welcome change for a variety of reasons. They may have been critical of the old system and welcome change as it confirms their view that change is overdue. They may also see a restructuring of the organisation as an opportunity to relocate to a different department where the work will be more personally fulfilling or where there are prospects of improving their career. There will also be individuals who regard change positively and welcome innovation as exciting. When leading change it is important to recognise the different responses to change and ensure that each individual's reaction is understood and respected.

Change and stress

Understanding the impact of change on individuals means recognising that it can create anxiety, uncertainty and stress (Carnall, 1991). In his description of the individual's reaction to change Carnall suggests that even where people are committed to change they may still experience stress as there is no guarantee that the changes being implemented will work and lead to improvement. Individuals who are involved in implementation are likely to have a heavy workload, working long hours, dealing with problems as they arise and trying to overcome the doubts of those who question the need for change. Carnall identifies role strain and change as major sources of stress, arising from factors such as not being involved in decision making, having poor management support, maintaining standards of performance under difficult circumstances, and having responsibility for people who are uncooperative. All of these factors are likely to occur during change and can affect the individual's self-esteem and consequently their performance. Carnall describes individuals having four main needs during change:

- they need intelligible information, in a form they can understand
- they need to develop new skills, including the skills of new relationships
- they need support to deal with problems and be encouraged to try out new ways of working, and this is where training and technical support can help
- they need to be treated with empathy and this is seen as the most important factor. Where those leading change attempt to understand the situation from the perspective of the person experiencing change, then their support is more likely to be viewed positively.

None of this is guaranteed to reduce the stress of change for individuals, but where those leading change carefully plan and manage implementation sensitively, taking into account the needs of individuals affected, then practical and positive steps can be taken to support individuals as they cope with change.

Why individuals may resist change

When individuals are faced with change in their work environment they may be resistant for a variety of reasons. Where change is imposed from above without prior consultation, then anxiety about the future is likely to lead to resistance to change. This is exacerbated where senior managers fail to fully explain the need for change. Resistance is also likely to be present when individuals who have prospered under current organisational arrangements are threatened with changes and may have natural concerns about what the future holds for them. Significant organisational change can also raise concerns about the future and what this will mean for the individual. Change can also mean that social structures are severed when long established work relationships are disrupted by new structural arrangements.

Mullins (2005) describes some of the most common reasons that individuals resist change.

- **Selective perception** describes an individual's picture of the 'real' world that can result in a biased view of a particular situation which fits most comfortably with the individual's perception of reality. An example is the stereotyped views held by an individual who fails to acknowledge the reality of a situation and can result in resistance to change even where this would advantage the individual and the service.
- **Habit**. This is when individuals tend to respond to situations in an established and accustomed manner. This response may serve as a means of comfort and security. Change which threatens established habits, if these habits are well established and require little effort, may be resisted. The extent of resistance will depend on the degree that the individual feels there is personal advantage in the proposed changes.
- **Inconvenience or loss of freedom** can mean that change means work life is more difficult or reduces freedom of action or increased control is likely to be resisted. Examples can include where changes in organisational routines inconvenience individuals.
- **Economic implications** are likely to be a factor in resistance if the proposed change threatens to reduce, directly or indirectly, income or other rewards, or increases workload without commensurate improvement in reward. This factor can also be considered when job security is threatened.
- **Security in the past** describes the harking back to former, more comfortable ways when faced with new or unfamiliar ideas or methods. Tried and trusted methods provide a feeling of security at times of change.
- **Fear of the unknown** is common where individuals are confronted with the unknown and can cause anxiety or fear. This is seen where there are major changes in organisational structures or the introduction of new working techniques. The degree of anxiety can be such as to prevent individuals taking on greater responsibility or promotion for fear of failure.

In providing guidance for managers who are responding to resistance, Moss Kanter (1985) makes a number of suggestions that managers need to consider if change is to be managed effectively.

Change is something individuals often feel is **done to them** or imposed from by outside factors. Therefore, they feel they have little control over their situation and are more likely to be resistant to change and more defensive about the aspects of their work they can control. As ownership is important in securing an individual's commitment to change, the more they can participate in the decisions about change, the more they are likely to feel positive.

As the process of change is often begun **without leaders explaining fully what is involved** and what each stage of the implementation requires, or where they are lukewarm or half-hearted about the change, it is likely to leave individuals with too much uncertainty or doubtful about the commitment of those leading change. To overcome these doubts leaders need to demonstrate their commitment to the changes proposed and explain fully what is involved in implementation.

Where decisions about change are **sprung on individuals** without warning, this can result in resistance as they have insufficient time to consider them or think through what the changes mean for them. This can leave individuals with the feeling that they are not trusted if managers do not provide them with information and advance warning when changes are needed. Giving information early about the need for change demonstrates respect for the individual and allows them time to adjust their thinking and consider what the change means for them.

By its very nature change requires individuals to question familiar **routines and habits**. As routines are essential for effective functioning in the workplace, changing them means the behaviour individuals took for granted has to be questioned and can cause resistance. When making changes, it is important to minimise or reduce the number of 'differences' introduced by change, leaving as many habits and routines in place as possible. There is likely to be greater commitment to change and more successful implementation when change appears to be a continuation of the past rather than an abrupt break with former habits and routines.

Introducing changes can mean individuals have to develop **new skills and ways of working**, which can raise doubts about future competence. They are likely to ask questions such as '*I can do this?*' and '*Will I have the skills to operate in the new way?*'. These concerns may not be verbalised, but can be reasons why change is threatening and resisted. It is also necessary to recognise that when change is implemented rapidly it can require individuals to change too quickly and fail to take account of the time needed by some individuals to adjust to new demands. Recognising that levels of performance may drop as individuals grapple with new ways of working and developing new skills, and identifying the barriers that make it difficult for them to work in new ways is a key part of managing change. To respond to such concerns it is essential to provide training and development opportunities and to give individuals the opportunity to practice new skills in a safe environment without feeling they are being judged or losing face when they do not perform immediately at the standard required.

Changes can have **ripple effects** beyond their intended target and disrupt the plans and activities of individuals even though they are not directly involved in the changes. These are typically when long-standing personal and domestic arrangements have to change following a change in organisational routines. When change is introduced it is important to consider how it might affect individuals and their personal arrangements, introducing change as flexibly as possible rather than as an abrupt change to enable those affected to make new arrangements. This kind of sensitive consideration can help build commitment to change rather than resistance.

Where change means **more work** for the individual, whether it is more energy, more time or effort, or more mental preoccupation, this can lead to resistance if they do not want to put in the extra effort. To enable individuals to make the extra effort, compensation, or at least acknowledgement in some form, can help move attitudes from resistance to commitment. If financial or other rewards are not possible, at least recognition that the individual is making an extra effort needs acknowledging.

When change is proposed it can reveal **past grievances** that get in the way of moving forward with change. Grievances may be suppressed while things are stable, but surface when individuals are asked to change. Where grievances hinder change it is important to resolve them or at least acknowledge them so that an individual's relationship with the organisation can be repaired.

Lastly, it is necessary to acknowledge that change can be **a real threat** to the individual. The political reality of change in organisations can mean winners and losers. Where there are threats to an individual's job they should be told personally and hear about it early, rather than late. Managers need to face this and not pretend otherwise. In any change where there is loss, whether it is established routines, the comfort of habits, traditions that are important, or the break-up of long-standing relationships, it is important that individuals are supported to let go of the past, to 'mourn it' and acknowledge the past was valued and now it is time to move on. Without these rituals it risks taking resentments into the future which can increase resistance, but also damage the psychological contract between the organisation and the individual.

Assessing the possible reasons for resistance

What these examples of resistance point to is that those leading change and managers who are tasked with implementation operationally often fail to give time to assessing the likelihood of resistance and who might resist change and for what reasons. Because individuals can resist change for myriad reasons, a considered assessment is essential. If assessment has been made of the many possibilities which apply to those affected by change it can help managers select the most appropriate way to overcome resistance. This can save time later when implementation is hindered by resistance that is difficult to overcome, or where change is pushed through in a climate of resentment without the individual's commitment if it is to be effective.

Where there is fundamental disagreement

One form of resistance which is particularly difficult to challenge is where an individual fundamentally disagrees with a proposed change, particularly where this challenges their deeply held beliefs about the purpose of a service. Upton and Brooks (1995) describe how difficult this is for the manager who can do little to change the individual's views, except demonstrating where you feel the change will improve the service and does not undermine the values of the organisation. It may also be possible to demonstrate it working effectively in another location or by exposing them to wider trends in services (see case study on p.106), and the objective facts to try to change their perception of the change, and see it more positively. In the end you have to implement the change without them as you cannot allow one person to block change. Ultimately, if they are unable to reconcile their views with the changes that are taking place they may have to work in the new situation however reluctantly, or choose to work elsewhere.

Managers' responsibility

As all the emphasis tends to be placed on the individual who resists change, it is necessary to balance this perspective with the need for those leading change to reflect on their own thinking and behaviour. Have they thought through in sufficient detail the implications of change? Have they assessed the need for additional resources to support implementation? Have they communicated sufficiently with frontline staff the need for change? Have they ensured that support mechanisms and training opportunities are in place to support staff who feel threatened by change? These questions help us to see that resistance is often a reaction to the respective responsibilities of key people.

Figure 6.1: Readiness and capability chart

	Readiness			Capability		
Individuals	**High**	**Medium**	**Low**	**High**	**Medium**	**Low**
Team leader	X			X		
Senior practitioner		X		X		
Social worker (1)	X				X	
Social worker (2)			X			X

This sample readiness and capability chart plots individuals important to change in practice and their commitment.

Key

Team leader: Committed to the change and has skills to successfully manage implementation.

Senior practitioner: Has some doubts about the timing of the change, although highly skilled. Needs reassurance that change is manageable.

First social worker: Enthusiastic about the change, but will need some additional training to meet skill level needed.

Second social worker: Unenthusiastic about the change and does not have sufficient skills. Will need support and training to identify concerns and to increase skill level.

Resistance as feedback

Much of the discussion about resistance has tended to describe it in orthodox terms, with the managers on one side pressing for change and the staff on the other finding myriad reasons to block change. Smale (1998) questions this over-simplistic view and asks whether it is the change itself or the supposed conservative nature of individuals that really creates resistance. Rather he sees resistance as feedback, suggesting that those pressing for change are probably not managing the process well and that they need to listen more to others and change their own thinking and behaviour. This would certainly lead us to see resistance as an appropriate response to change where it leads to a review of ill-considered plans that have not been thought through sufficiently, or where change has been hastily introduced without proper consultation with those affected. For those tasked with implementation at the front line, resistance to plans that are unlikely to be successful is a necessary brake on action. This is particularly so when the blame for failed change strategies is laid at the door of frontline staff, rather than those who were unable to appreciate the complexity of implementation.

Case study

The impact of change

A health authority made a decision to close a hospital unit for severely disabled children after it was reviewed by an external panel of experts who reported that the care provided was not meeting the needs of the children. Although the physical care provided was of a high standard, the unit had a number of shortcomings including insufficient social and educational opportunities for the children due to the medically orientated regime, staff who had not been provided with training in current methods and were relying on an outdated model of care, with the location of the unit limiting access to ordinary community facilities.

The decision was made to close the unit and transfer the children to community based facilities based on ordinary houses, with the shift of emphasis towards social rather than health care. The announcement of this decision came as a complete shock to staff and elicited a strong reaction. There was immediate resistance to the plan as the staff felt that the care they provided was of a high standard and that the needs of severely disabled children were best met in a traditional health care setting. A strong campaign of resistance to the decision was mounted by some staff, including seeking backing from parents and general practitioners. Equally, the health authority worked to explain the reasons for the decision and the improvements that would be made to the lives of the children if they were able to live in more domestic scale surroundings and participate in more community activities, while at the same time having their health needs recognised.

Over a period of one year a process consultant worked with the staff team, holding regular group and individual meetings to enable them to express the feelings about the change. One of the key findings from work with the staff team was their lack of awareness and understanding of current models of care. Arrangements were made for them to learn about new models of care and to visit other services that had made similar changes. Alongside these activities the authority worked with staff on identifying their future options as some staff decided that they would transfer to other health service work rather than move into what were seen as social care roles. Over time a small core of staff became committed to the change and successfully moved into the community settings and expressed considerable satisfaction with the new service. Some of those staff most vehemently opposed to the change subsequently became committed enthusiasts and were influential leaders in the new service. For other staff they made a personal decision to transfer to posts in the health authority outside the learning disability service.

Comment

We learn a number of things from this case example about the impact of change on individuals. The reaction of staff and their resistance to change was understandable. The decision was announced without prior consultation with staff who were shocked by the announcement that the unit would close. The feelings of disbelief were evident. The decision was not believed as the staff felt they were providing a good service, and had not been exposed to other models of care that demonstrated how the children's development could be improved by living in a more normal family-like environment. The change was seen as detrimental to the children, who staff believed would not survive outside of the hospital environment. As the staff had had few developmental opportunities, they were unaware of the changes that were taking place nationally, as policy on the residential care of disabled children changed.

Some practical steps to support people through change

Finally, Amos (1996) offers some practical advice for managers confronted with resistance, recognising that working with individuals takes time and effort, but is a worthwhile investment that can help individuals view change more positively. A number of these issues have been covered earlier in this and previous chapters, but Amos's points act as a valuable aide memoire when managing change.

Preparation

- Be positive about the change you are introducing
- Set clear objectives
- Get the timing right wherever possible
- Ensure that there are adequate resources available to help ease implementation, and don't underestimate how long change will take

Information

- Be sure of your facts when you are discussing what has to change
- Check things out – 'look before you leap'
- Check what things don't need to change, and make sure they are unaffected
- Look at the change issues from all angles

Involvement

- Ask those involved for their views and feedback
- Delegate tasks where possible as involving individuals will increase interest and commitment to change
- Get those individuals directly affected by change to participate in making decisions if possible, as early as possible
- Involve individuals who have knowledge or expertise, particularly among your own staff

Communication

- Be honest about the need for change, and the extent of change needed
- Don't withhold information – communicate as much as you can about the proposed change
- Explain the circumstances that create the need for change
- Encourage two-way communication
- Make change sound achievable and logical
- Sell the change to individuals, don't force it on them

Awareness

- Encourage individuals to get involved in the change process
- Keep in touch with the change process and how it is progressing
- Recognise the effort and contribution of individuals
- Recognise that resistance is healthy and natural, and work with individuals to help them understand the need for change
- Review and check that the changes are working
- Squash rumours that undermine the change process

Summary

This chapter has explored some of the human factors in change and how individuals may respond to change. We have seen that there is a close relationship between how individuals view their work, their relationship with their line manager and the wider organisation and their willingness to change. An understanding of the change transition and how individuals may react to the demands of change are important. With greater understanding of the impact of change on individuals, managers are in a better position to introduce change more effectively. In any change proposal there is the potential for resistance, particularly when long established ways of working or habits are under threat. Resistance is not necessarily bad if it enables managers to reflect on change which is hasty and poorly thought out and the view that resistance can be seen as helpful feedback – no matter how unwelcome to the manager – has some validity, when one considers the history of badly managed change which damages organisations and demoralises staff.

References

Amos JA (1996) *Starting to Manage: How to prepare yourself for a more responsible role at work*. Plymouth: How to Books.

Carnall C (1991) *Managing Change (Self development for managers)*. London: Routledge.

CIPD (2004) *Managing the Psychological Contract (factsheet)*. London: Chartered Institute of Personnel and Development. Available at: www.cipd.co.uk

CIPD (2005) *Managing Change: The role of the psychological contract*. London: Chartered Institute of Personnel and Development. Available at: www.cipd.co.uk

Fulop L & Linstead S (2004) Motivation and meaning. In: S Linstead, L Fulop & S Lilley (Eds) *Management and Organization: A critical text*. Basingstoke: Macmillan.

Gilbert P (2005) *Leadership: Being effective and remaining human*. Lyme Regis: Russell House Publishing.

Hutchinson S & Purcell J (2003) *Bringing Policies to Life: The vital role of the front line managers in people development*. London: Chartered Institute of Personnel and Development.

Moss Kanter R (1985) Managing the human side of change. *Management Review* **74** 52–56.

Mullins L (2005) *Management and Organisational Behaviour* (7th edition). Harlow: Pearson Education.

Pate J, Martin G & Staines H (2000) Exploring the relationship between psychological contracts and organizational change: a process model and case study evidence. *Strategic Change* **9** (8) 481–493.

Rousseau DM (1996) Changing the deal while keeping the people. *Academy of Management Executive* **18** (1) 50–59.

Smale G (1998) *Managing Change Through Innovation*. London: The Stationery Office.

Skye E, Meddings S & Dimmock B (2003) Theories for understanding people. In: Henderson J & Atkinson D (Eds) *Managing Care in Context*. London: Routledge.

Upton T & Brooks B (1995) *Managing Change in the NHS*. Buckingham: Open University Press.

Woodruffe C (1999) *Winning the Talent War: A strategic approach to attracting, developing and retaining the best people*. Chichester: Wiley.

Chapter 7

Managing the change process

Key points

- Importance of setting the direction of change
- Agree the level of individual participation in change
- Decisions about the correct timescales for change
- Key roles and responsibilities for supporting implementation
- Force field analysis and barriers to change
- Choosing appropriate styles of managing change
- Evaluating change and learning lessons for the future

Introduction

Managing change is where the detailed work of change starts. The range of activities when large scale change is considered is large and complex and demands an understanding of the different stages of implementation and those who need to be involved. Managing change includes being clear about the direction of change, the level of staff participation and the timescales for implementation. Key staff can include change agents and consultants who are responsible for ensuring that implementation is achieved. The demands change makes on individuals can result in forces both for and against change and the force field analysis can help us understand how change can be progressed. Finally, the chapter describes the importance of evaluation, which is often a neglected stage in the change process.

Direction: the aim and objectives of change

Once a decision has been taken to initiate change, the action then turns to fulfilling the aim of the change and its subsequent implementation. Managers leading change need to ensure that they effectively communicate in broad terms the sense of direction for the organisation and are sufficiently upbeat and inspiring that the staff of the organisation can unite behind the message. People affected by the change need to believe that the managers leading the change have a clear vision of where they are going and that they can be trusted to support them when they hit difficulties. This is where leadership is critical in setting the direction and purpose of the change and not overloading people with information. Establishing the general direction rather than a detailed blueprint is sufficient as too rigid a plan will not leave sufficient flexibility for frontline staff to work out their own solutions to problems as they occur during implementation. Flexibility is also important as change rarely proceeds in a straightforward direction during implementation, as the practical realities of changing systems and processes inevitably leads to modifications and adaptations along the way.

Decisions about the level of staff participation

Once the reasons for the proposed change and the aim are clear and understood by those who will be affected, decisions need to be made about the extent that staff are encouraged to get involved with the detailed planning of implementation. A range of different approaches are worth consideration, as described by Child (2005).

- Where there is broad agreement about the aim and objectives of change, but there is disagreement about how to actually achieve the change, then participation can be helpful as those staff affected will be more motivated to engage in discussion about the best way forward with the likelihood of consensus around the change proposal emerging.
- Where there is strong opposition to the proposed change, with fundamental disagreement with senior managers, then consultation and participation may only mean creating further opportunities for obstructing proposals put forward and delaying implementation. Here change may have to be pushed through, but this will depend on the management's power to direct change.
- Where the proposed change will affect people's employment, it is ethical to discuss with them what options are available. Where organisational change involves redundancy or redeployment, staff need to know the shape of the new structures and staffing required as quickly as possible as this will enable them to feel more secure or negotiate the best possible terms depending on the decisions made.

Where there is the possibility of agreement, the participation of staff in the design and implementation of change is seen as important. It offers the opportunity for the reasoning behind the change to be explained and discussed critically, and it is more likely that the active contribution to change can help build commitment and increase the chances of successful implementation.

Child (2005) argues that implementing change requires a great deal of information, for example, current problems, activities, decision points, costs and personnel, that are likely only to be known in detail by those who have expertise in the areas affected.

Participation is therefore essential if the change is to be grounded in the reality of the situation and draws on the skills and experience of staff who will implement the change. Participation also offers the opportunity for managers leading change to learn about the attitudes and values held by staff that can help them understand the impact of change on individuals and help in future decisions to introduce change. On the other hand, staff discussion with managers will enable them to learn about the need for change from a wider organisational perspective.

Increasing participation: the value of the diagonal slice

The team responsible for change can use the example of the diagonal slice. This would take staff from across different sections and levels of the organisation with the aim of the 'slice' of levels increasing involvement and expertise. It can also serve to assess the organisation's response to change, and to monitor the progress of change. It is suggested that you do not choose individuals who have direct line relationships with each other (Broome, 1990).

Figure 7.1: Diagonal slice

Headquarters	Residential services	Residential homes (registered manager)	Residential homes (front line)	
X				CEO
	X			Department head
		X		Registered manager
			X	Care assistant

A diagonal slice of staff in a third sector residential service for older people where there are proposals to develop a respite care service across a range of homes.

Timescales for change

When setting the timescale for change it is crucial to get the balance correct. An urgent timeframe carries the risks that this will be too challenging and may mean it is impossible to implement with the resources available and within the timescales set. A lack of a clear timeframe can mean that staff do not have clear targets to achieve, or if the timeframe is so long it can drain urgency and commitment from the process. When deciding timeframes, there is a further balance to be struck between the time taken for consultation on the implementation and the chances of change succeeding. Evidence from research (Vrakking, 1997) shows that there is an inverse relationship between the time taken to implement change and the extent of change ultimately achieved. Although participation is seen as important when implementing change, too much consultation can reduce the effectiveness of the change process. This is particularly so in large complex organisations where there is the need for rapid action, for example, in the case of forced transformational change. In this type of situation extensive consultation may not be practical when an organisation's future is at risk. Nevertheless, participation, in spite of the potential difficulties, provides an opportunity that can have significant benefits in supporting change and reducing resistance.

Visual representation of the timeframe for change

One way to create a visual representation of the timeframe with the individual tasks identified is to use a Gantt chart (see Figure 7.2 opposite). This is a bar chart that shows the timing of activities as they occur across time and provides you with the basis for scheduling when the different tasks of implementation need to be undertaken. It is based on the concept that some activities in the process of change are dependent on other activities being completed first. It can help you work out a critical path when implementation needs to be completed by a particular date. Once a change project is underway it enables you to monitor whether it is on schedule, and if a task is not completed on time it provides evidence for you to take the action to put it back on schedule. The level of detail will be dependent on the timescale for the change and the number of individuals who are directly involved.

Figure 7.2: Gantt chart

Area	Activity	Responsibility	March	April	May	June
Designing	Specify training need	BM				
	Agree methods	JS				
	Design training programme	DN				
Production	Write programme	DN				
	Prepare trainers manual	DN				
	Print material	DJ				
Training the trainers	Design training programme	JS				
	Allocate dates	JS				
	Train trainers	JS/DN				
Deliver training	First four sessions	Trainers				
	Review impact	BM			8th May launch	

Example of the design, production and delivery of a training programme to support organisational change.

Figure 7.3: Contingency chart

Activity	Potential problem	Likelihood (1-10)	Possible cause	Preventative activity	Contingency plan

This chart is used alongside the Gantt chart to assess any likely contingencies.

Key roles and responsibilities

There will be a number of key roles and responsibilities in introducing change depending on the scale and complexity of the change proposed. Where the focus is organisation-wide then a large number of individual roles may be needed, including a senior manager who acts as a sponsor of change, change champions, project steering group leader and participants, consultants with specific expertise and other specialists. Each of these individuals will have a specific role in implementing change and may need to be supplemented by others depending on the complexity of the change process.

Upton and Brooks (1995) describe the importance of recognising the different levels of influence and responsibility for decisions in change. Identifying who needs to be consulted and kept informed is important as change can be undermined by the failure to involve key people at the appropriate stage in implementation. They suggest that a useful way to identify those involved is through a responsibility chart (see Figure 7.4 below) which indicates the level of responsibility key people have for a task using five categories:

A: powers of approval and veto

R: responsible for action and delivery of results once approval has been given

P: provide resources

I: to be kept informed, but otherwise not involved

C: consulted before decisions taken.

They suggest that there should not be more that one 'R' for each task, and if there is more than one person responsible for a particular task, it should be divided into two distinct parts and responsibility allocated for each part. Similarly they suggest keeping the As to a minimum, otherwise decision-making is made more difficult.

Figure 7.4: Responsibility chart

Name

Role	Head of department	Clinical lead/ matron	Team leader/ sister	Staff nurse	Prescriber	Other professionals
Concept of administering IV therapy in patients home rather than hospital	A	C	C		C	
Translating concept into policy for a new service		R (lead)	R (training)	C	I	I
Implementation of new policy		I	R	C	C	
Monitoring and evaluation of effectiveness of new service	I	R				

A simplified example of individual responsibilities in relation to establishing a new service which provides intravenous therapy in patients' homes.

Change agents

We have seen in a previous chapter that those leading change at a senior level are not necessarily in the best position to do the detailed work needed with staff at the implementation phase. This is where the change agent plays an important role in championing the change (and is sometimes described as the product champion) with the energy and commitment to push change through. Change agents are formally or informally employed to implement innovation or introduce new working methods to others.

Smale (1998) suggests that you map all the people in your organisation who are likely to champion the change and those who may oppose it. It is important not to prejudge who is likely to prove an effective change agent as these individuals can be found in all sorts of roles and levels in organisations, although they are likely to have leadership characteristics that enable them to influence others. Smale suggests that the ideal change agent is likely to be an opinion leader who has an influence on the methods used by others. Their status or personal prestige means that others see them as models of good practice. In this role the change agent works with a wide range of people, and is both part of the organisation but also sufficiently detached that they can act as an honest broker between individuals and groups to help them deal with issues that are blocking implementation.

Johnson and Scholes (2002) describe the change agent as having a range of approaches when working with an organisation on change. These include emphasising collaboration and feedback, which encourages people to contribute in developing the change process; sympathy with the notion of the learning organisation; focusing on improving relationships between people in the organisation and the environment where they work so that learning can take place; and finally, adopting an interventionist approach that seeks to identify signals and symbols of change by which assumptions can be challenged and questioned and routines changed.

In describing the role of change agents in strategic change, Johnson and Scholes identify four key areas.

1. The ability to undertake detailed analysis and at the same time be visionary about the future. To achieve the credibility they need to have insight about the future, yet be action-oriented about making things happen.
2. The ability to challenge the status quo, maintaining credibility and taking people with them at the same time as attacking taken for granted and current ways of working.

3. The ability to communicate strategy in a way that encapsulates complex issues in everyday language that people can understand.

4. The ability to maintain performance in the organisation while breaking down old assumptions and old ways of working which potentially jeopardise it.

In a breakdown of the main competences needed by change agents, Buchanan and Boddy (1992) identify five main areas where change agents need to be competent.

1. **Goals:** sensitivity to personnel, their perceptions, the external environment and the way these impact on the proposed change.

2. **Roles:** the ability to develop teams, bring together key stakeholders and establish effective working groups, defining and delegating responsibility clearly.

3. **Communication:** enthusiasm and commitment in support of change, and the ability to motivate and develop commitment in others. Interpersonal skills, with the ability to communicate the need for change.

4. **Negotiation:** selling ideas to others and negotiating with key players for resources or change in procedures and to resolve conflicts.

5. **Managing upwards:** political awareness, identifying potential coalitions and balancing goals and perceptions, influencing skills in order to gain commitment to plans and ideas from sceptics and those resistant to change. A helicopter perspective, with the ability to stand back and take a broader view of priorities.

Smale (1998) describes some of the important dimensions of being a change agent. These include having an honest and straightforward approach towards the people implementing change about the difficulties and constraints likely to be met along the road to implementation, being open and honest in communications, and genuinely listening to others. This means the change agent has to value such behaviour in themselves and others. Straight and honest communication requires a degree of self-awareness with congruence between actions and beliefs. Similarly, honesty with senior managers about the perceptions and experiences of frontline staff is also important. Smale cautions against the danger of maintaining the fiction that everything is working well when there are problems. There are also particular risks with 'consultation' exercises where senior managers have already made up their mind and staff can recognise the activity as a pretence at consultation.

Using outside consultants

It may be considered necessary to use outside consultants to support the process of change where there is concern that the organisation has insufficient resources or technical knowledge to effectively manage the change process itself. Consultants can bring a number of advantages to an organisation including:

- experience of working with a range of different services that can help change managers better understand their problems and suggest ways of overcoming difficulties based on previous consulting experience in similar organisations
- act as a sounding board for senior managers and other change team managers where an independent opinion is helpful in questioning current assumptions and offering reassurance when the organisation is getting things right
- an impartiality to internal politics and providing a degree of objectivity and breadth of experience which can help managers state more frankly their concerns and help staff experiencing change to think more openly and positively about how to implement change.

Expert and process consultants

There are two approaches to consultancy that are relevant to different organisational needs. The expert consultant is someone who is employed to offer technical or specialist advice on what to do and how to solve specific problems. They are usually consulted for a short duration. In contrast, the process consultant is employed to help the organisation understand how to achieve fundamental change through work at systems and group and individual levels. This is more likely to be a longer-term engagement, although this will vary depending on the problems facing the organisation and how quickly and positively staff adapt to change. Ideally, process consultants need skills in problem solving, coaching, team building and staff development.

Choosing the right consultant

It is important that the right consultant is engaged. Reputation and track record are important, along with experience in health and social care services, as well as an understanding of the values and culture of public services. The experience of consultancies promoting change models that are inappropriate and insensitive to public services have made many managers and staff rightly wary of consultants. Other important factors include the correct skills and experience for the problem, flexibility in responding to needs, sufficient resources to complete the contract, and costs and value for money.

Briefing consultants

It is important that the consultant is clear about the brief and what help is needed. The brief should include the following:

- information on the organisation, including how it is managed
- changes facing the organisation
- change proposals
- perception of the problem and how the consultant could help
- the work you want the consultant to do
- terms of reference for the project
- outcome/benefits expected
- timescale for the project
- estimate of the budget available
- who is responsible for managing the project
- how the outcome will be evaluated.

(Department of Employment, 1991)

Where process consultancy is needed, the consultant will spend time getting to know the organisation and understanding how it operates in order to identify problems from different perspectives and suggest alternatives. These are then fed back to decision makers so that an accurate assessment of problems can be agreed and accepted. The important role of the process consultant is to understand the real issues that are blocking change and present findings that enable an action plan to be developed by managers. The process itself can lead to uncomfortable responses from those people whose status and responsibilities are likely to be affected by suggested changes. Where managers have to accept that they need to change, the consultant can be helpful in posing questions that internal staff would find difficult to ask.

Resources

An essential part of planning the implementation of change is identifying the resources that will be needed to ensure success. None of this will be easy if there is not sufficient commitment from a strong leadership with a change strategy that is desirable and at a cost the organisation can manage. If the change is sufficiently important then resources need to be allocated so that it can take place within the timescale set. It is essential that any large scale change acknowledges the extent of the investment needed. There is a tendency for change to be planned without sufficient weight given to the level of resources needed. You should certainly think about having sufficient people, the time that they will need, and adequate financial and administrative support as being essentials. It is also important to identify the likely range of resources at an early stage in planning, although this is likely to change as the reality of implementation proceeds and unforeseen events and issues emerge. The following should certainly be seen as essential in most large scale change proposals:

- key personnel
- additional staff as needed
- cost of converting to a new system or process
- new equipment
- training costs
- consultancy and other technical support
- evaluation of the outcomes of the change
- unforeseen contingencies.

Bryson (2004) suggests that it is also important to have sufficient capacity built into the change process if possible to provide backup if things go wrong, as they are likely to do with any large scale change.

Forces for and against change

When you are managing change it is useful to understand what forces are 'for' and 'against' change. The force field analysis is a well established technique, originally developed by Lewin (1951), and is a diagrammatic way of mapping the forces that are keeping a particular situation in the current state of equilibrium, between the forces pushing for change (driving forces) and the forces resisting change (restraining forces). If these forces are of equal strength they are said to be in a state of equilibrium and change cannot take place. To bring about change there has to be an increase in the driving forces or a decrease in the resisting forces. The diagram below demonstrates the forces present in the case study of a hospital for disabled children which faced closure (see Chapter 6).

Figure 7.5: Force field analysis

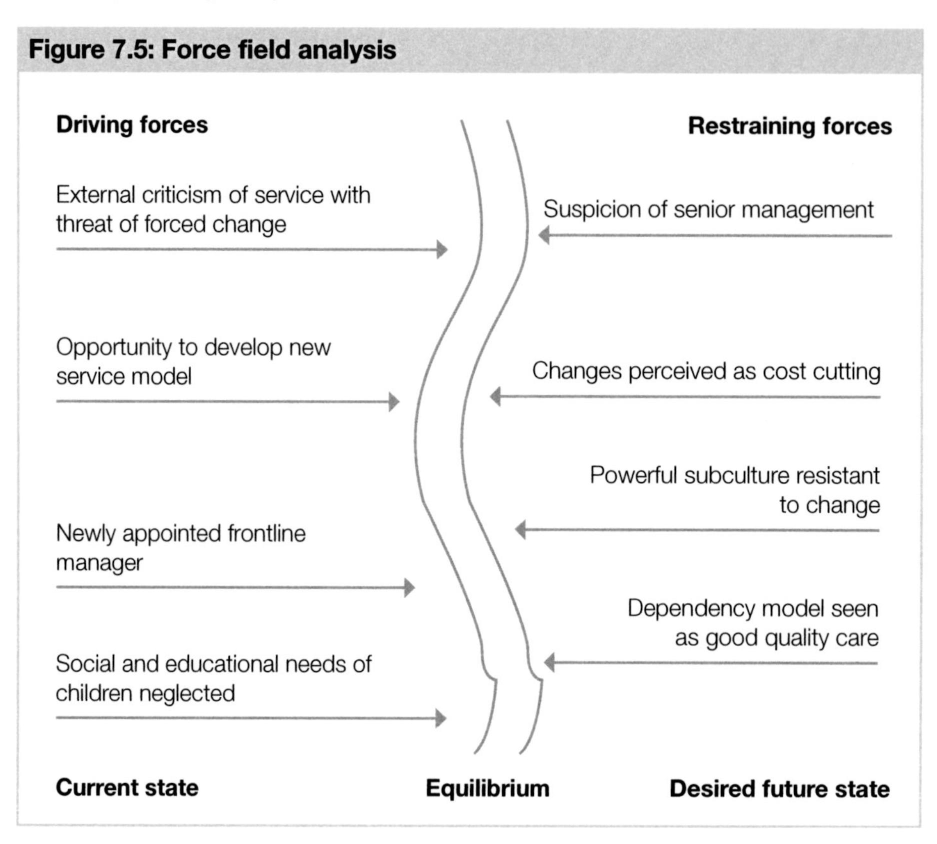

Lewin's three phases of change

Closely associated with the force field analysis is Lewin's three phase model of change. These comprise: unfreezing, changing and refreezing.

Unfreezing

This is the state when the need for change is recognised and action is taken to unfreeze existing attitudes and behaviour. It is seen as necessary to generate support for change and reduce resistance. Johnson and Scholes (2002) see this as breaking down cultural inertia and resistance to change through challenging the prevailing paradigm so that a new strategy can be followed.

They describe how changes in the external environment can act as unfreezing mechanisms, such as changes in demand for services or a deteriorating market position. Where these external signs are less clear, managers may exaggerate signs of problems to signal that current ways of working are under challenge. At the stage when attitudes are beginning to unfreeze, flux may occur with different views surfacing with a rise in political activity and conflict. Johnson and Scholes see this as useful as it enables a healthy debate about different points of view to surface and challenge taken for granted attitudes.

Changing

The second stage is where the need for change is recognised and resistance has been reduced. New attitudes or behaviours are developed and the implementation of change takes place. This stage can also include the experimentation and testing of new systems and procedures, and changes in personnel resulting from the change. When the new systems and processes are established, a new equilibrium is reached.

Refreezing

This final stage describes the changes that take place when new attitudes and behaviours develop. Changes that have been introduced are stabilised, supported and reinforced through support mechanisms with the intention of promoting the internalisation of new attitudes and behaviours. This is also the stage when the change is evaluated to ensure that it is fully integrated into the new way of working.

Coulshed and Mullender (2006) see the force field analysis as a practical tool that is helpful to the manager when carrying through change as it can help in making decisions about how to cope with the conflicts change can reveal. They highlight the risks to managers where there is a tendency to concentrate on arguing against those who speak out against change, rather than winning over and working with those who ally themselves with change. Practically they suggest that the manager should be aware when meeting staff about a proposed change to identify where there is support for the change, and where there are concerns. They nevertheless suggest some caution in relying too much on the force field analysis as some aspects of resistance, such as silent opposition and genuine indifference, are likely also to be restraining factors that can be missing from the analysis. They suggest that only detailed discussion is likely to reveal those who are quietly resistant towards change and that in using the force field analysis there could be a tendency to see change as a 'one-off' event rather than a process over time.

Although you will wish to maintain the important driving forces, paradoxically trying to increase them tends, in turn, to increase the restraining forces. A preferred focus is to work with staff to identify their concerns rather than trying to push through change which can lead to more resistance. Iles and Sutherland (2001) suggest that reducing resisting forces is preferable because it allows movement towards the desired state without increasing tension, which is likely to occur when driving forces are increased, which in turn results in an increase in resisting forces with increased tension. They point out that managers who placed their focus on the driving forces, rather than reducing the resisting ones, have in turn increased resistance and tension as a result. They also suggest that for the model to be useful to managers, the forces need to be identified perceptively, rigorously and objectively, and the means of addressing resisting forces needs to be creative.

Organisational factors that may create barriers to change

Mullins (2005) has described how organisations need to adapt to changes in the external environment if they are to prosper, but tend to be constrained by structures and processes that are designed to deal with the current situation rather than the future. He describes a range of defences that can become deeply rooted in organisations and inhibit change.

- **Organisational culture** can act as a powerful brake on change, particularly where it is long established. We have seen in Chapter 4 that organisational cultures can be slow to change and not easily influenced by management action. It may be difficult to understand why there is resistance to a proposed change unless there is an appreciation of the power of culture to shape responses to change.
- **Maintaining stability** is an important feature of large organisations, particularly in the public sector, which depend on formal hierarchies, structures, and defined roles based on established procedures and work methods. As a result, these bureaucratic organisations find it more difficult to respond to change. This is particularly apparent where there is strong central control or a 'command and control' style of management that blocks change, unless it is initiated at senior level. This approach to managing an organisation can also result in change proceeding at a snail's pace and failing to respond to changes in the environment sufficiently quickly.
- **Investment in resources** is necessary, to some degree, when change is planned and often not available due to pressures to drive down or reduce

costs. Where change is expected to take place within existing resources it can result in staff feeling overloaded and resentful of resource constraints.

- **Past contracts and agreements** can act as an inhibiting factor in change as organisations find it difficult to achieve the flexibility needed when they are limited by long standing contractual agreements that do not provide the flexibility for innovation or change. Resistance can increase where the proposed changes threaten job security.
- **Threats to power and influence** are ever present when significant change is considered. Change can present a threat to the power and influence of different groups within an organisation and their control over resources. Change may be resisted if individuals or groups perceive change will weaken their position in relation to others in the organisation.

All these defences against change are present to some extent in the case examples used in this book and demonstrate how organisational factors can influence individual behaviour and create resistance that has to be understood and managed if change is to be successful.

Strategies for managing change

When you are managing the change process you need to consider the most appropriate styles of management to adopt to achieve the aims. It is necessary to adopt different approaches as this will differ according to the organisational context and the degree of pressure for change (Caple, 1990; Johnson & Scholes, 2002). The following styles describe a range of approaches, with different combinations of style adopted according to organisational context and the degree and urgency of the change required.

Education and communication are used when staff need to learn new skills which are crucial for working in new ways. Communicating the vision through meeting with those working at the front line, testing out the vision and reinforcing it is an essential role for change managers.

Collaboration and participation are used as a means of engaging with those affected by the change, asking them to help design the process and thereby increasing ownership and commitment to the change.

Intervention is used when a change agent or others are given delegated responsibility to work with staff on particular aspects of the change process, including ideas generated, detailed planning or the development of rationales for change.

Direction is used when those leading the service use their authority to set the direction, means and speed of change. Closely associated with this style is coercion, where change is imposed through the use of managerial power. These styles may be used when an organisation is facing a crisis and survival is heavily dependent on rapid change.

Whichever methods are used – and most change processes use a combination of methods – there are advantages and disadvantages. A management style based on education and communication, and collaboration and participation, can be time consuming, although likely to increase ownership and commitment to change. Intervention, direction and coercion have advantages of speed, but risk perceptions of manipulation, or at worst, non-acceptance by staff. To a great extent, the urgency, scale and readiness for change will dictate the best style to adopt. Planned incremental change will favour a more participative approach, whereas forced transformational change will favour a more directive approach.

Figure 7.6: Strategies for managing change

Strategy	Advantages	Disadvantages	Context
Educative	Education and training used to increase understanding and commitment to change	Time-consuming Resource intensive	Incremental change Long-term transformational change
Participative	Involving wide range of individuals to develop change strategy	Time-consuming Resource intensive Inappropriate strategy may be developed	Incremental change Long-term transformational change
Expert-led	Change process guided by changing managment experts, often external consultants	Low involvement Risk of feeling manipulated by experts	Transformational change
Direction/ coercion	Change implemented rapidly when organisation in state of crisis and survival at risk	High resistance, unless crisis understood	Forced transformational change

Based on Caple (1990) and Johnson and Scholes (2002).

Case study

Managing change

A social services department was faced with severe cutbacks following a poor financial settlement. A decision had to be made about the future of the department's homes for older people. The homes were institutional in character and urgently needed improvement. They were also in a poor state of repair and needed significant upgrading. The local authority had not transferred any of its services to the independent sector at that point, but was faced with a stark choice of either transferring these services or closing them, as it did not have sufficient finance to upgrade them enough to meet the new regulatory standards that had recently been introduced. The director of social services felt he had no choice but to recommend a policy of transferring the homes to an independent sector provider.

The proposal to transfer the homes came as a shock to stakeholders (local politicians, staff and service users) who naturally reacted with disbelief. The director of social services and his senior team presented the stakeholders with the reality of the situation, and argued that unless the services were transferred to an external provider who could access funding to refurbish the homes, they would deteriorate further and eventually have to close. Recognising the need to be open and frank with stakeholders, the department organised a major consultation exercise, involving service users, staff, trade unions and politicians, about the future of the service. Following the consultation exercise where concerns about future service arrangements were discussed, four housing and care providers were shortlisted to present their plans for the homes to an audience of senior managers and stakeholder representatives. Following the presentations, a provider was selected and the homes were subsequently transferred successfully.

Comment

This case study describes some of the elements in the management of change. The director of social services set out the direction of change, recognising that this was likely to be opposed by a range of stakeholders. A timescale for change was also agreed as the local authority was under intense financial pressure to divest itself of the residential homes. Once the decision had been taken, a named senior manager was made responsible for the implementation of the change, with an external consultant who had experience of work with other local authorities employed to advise on the process of transferring services. The director of social services chose a style of managing the change which included communication and participation as far as was possible in view of the pressures on the department and the timescale for change. One of the lessons from this example is that although difficult decisions have to be made, and many were unhappy with the outcome, the manner in which stakeholders were treated helped avoid a damaging legacy of mistrust in senior managers.

Evaluating the effectiveness of the change strategy

Evaluation is the final stage in the process of change and one that is often neglected as managers fail to learn from their previous endeavours. Bryson (2004) argues that if we fail to evaluate change, how will we know precisely whether things are 'better' as a result of the implementation? He sees evaluation as having two main purposes. First, to find out if the goals set at the outset of the change process have been achieved, and second, whether the outputs and outcomes of change have been worth the time and effort required to implement them.

Iles (1997) poses some practical questions that those involved in change could reflect on at the evaluation stage.

Reviewing the change

- Did the change achieve its objectives?
- How closely did it mirror the plan?
- How did it differ, and if not, why did it differ?
- How do stakeholders feel about the change?
- Are there any further actions that need to be considered to achieve the objectives or to influence how stakeholders view the change?

Learning lessons for the future

- What would you do differently next time?
- Why would you do it differently, and how?

Iles's point is that without evaluating the change we lose the opportunity for learning that is rich and real, and without this stage learning is lost to both the individual and the organisation. Ideally, this process should encompass a wide range of stakeholders as this will make the learning process even richer. Bryson (2004) captures the importance of this process when he sees change as a learning process and that learning underpins successful change efforts, with those involved in developing new approaches and adapting them to the actual demands of change. If this learning is effective then implementation is likely to be more successful and the next round of change is likely to be better informed. Understanding the importance of evaluation means we can learn from the experience of change and hopefully ensure that future change projects are implemented more effectively. In this sense we can see change having no beginning or end, but a continuous cycle of renewal, which evaluation plays an important part in learning lessons for the future. Bryson leaves us with an important question about this vital last stage – how will we know whether, and in precisely what ways, things are 'better' as a result of the implemented changes?

Summary

This chapter has described some of the key issues in the process of managing change. It recognises that change management is a complex process that requires decisions about the extent to which staff are involved, the personnel needed to guide the change process, and the wide range of tools and techniques that can be used to ensure the more effective implementation of change. Finally, it suggests that evaluation is an important and often overlooked element in the change process, but one that can provide valuable learning on how to manage change effectively.

References

Broome A (1990) *Managing Change*. Basingstoke: Macmillan.

Bryson JM (2004) *Strategic Planning for Public and Nonprofit Organizations: A guide to strengthening and sustaining organizational achievement*. San Francisco: Jossey-Bass Publishers.

Buchanan D & Boddy D (1992) *The Expertise of the Change Agent: Public performance and backstage activity*. London: Prentice-Hall.

Caple T (1990) *Preparing People for Change: A handbook for trainers and managers*. Bristol: NHS Training Authority.

Child J (2005) *Organization, Contemporary Principles and Practice*. Oxford: Blackwell Publishing.

Coulshed V & Mullender A (2006) *Management in Social Work*. Basingstoke: Palgrave Macmillan.

Department of Employment (1991) *Choosing and Using a Consultant: A guide to managers and directors*. London: HMSO.

Iles V (1997) *Really Managing Health Care: The academic's perspective*. Buckingham: Open University Press.

Iles V & Sutherland K (2001) *Organisational Change: A review for health care managers, professionals and researchers* [online]. London: NCCSDO. Available at: http://www.sdo.nihr.ac.uk/files/adhoc/change-management-review.pdf (accessed June 2010).

Johnson G & Scholes K (2002) *Exploring Corporate Strategy* (6th edition). London: Prentice Hall.

Lewin K (1951) *Field Theory in Social Science*. New York: Harper and Row.

Mullins L (2005) *Management and Organisational Behaviour* (7th edition). Harlow: Prentice Hall.

Smale G (1998) *Managing Change Through Innovation*. London: The Stationery Office.

Vrakking W (1997) The implementation game. *Journal of Organisational Change Management* 8 (3) 31–46.

Upton T & Brooks B (1995) *Managing Change in the NHS*. Buckingham: Open University Press.

Chapter 8

Working with stakeholders

Key points

- The growth of the concept of stakeholders and their important role in change
- Stakeholder power, influence and expectations
- The stakeholder environment and mapping their power and influence
- Adopting a stakeholder's perspective and methods for learning their views

Introduction

Stakeholders are individuals, groups or other organisations that are affected in some way by the operations and activities of an organisation that is proposing to make changes, particularly of a strategic nature. When managers are making changes in their services they need to recognise the power and influence of stakeholders, both internal and external, who may have views about the intended changes and that may conflict with those of managers or professionals in the organisation. Typically, stakeholders include employees, users of a service and their relatives and carers, non-executive directors, elected politicians, purchasers of the services, trade unions, special interest groups, and other organisations working in partnership. The extent to which different stakeholders become active in relation to a proposed change will depend on the nature of the change being planned. When an organisation is preparing to make changes it needs to give attention to its stakeholders as the key to successful change is the satisfaction of stakeholders. This chapter will describe the importance of stakeholding, stakeholders' power and influence, techniques for assessing the likely response to proposed change and management responses, and how we can learn more about stakeholders' views.

Why are stakeholders important?

Although there will usually be general agreement among stakeholders that they wish to see an organisation prosper and deliver high quality services, among the different groups of stakeholders there is likely to be a range of views about the goals of a particular change. It is the relationship between different stakeholder groups and their power and influence on the organisation that constitutes the politics of change. It is therefore important that managers have an understanding of how power and politics among different stakeholder groups can influence the direction and content of change, and as a consequence are able to implement change strategies which recognise the political dimensions of change.

Although the decision to make changes can be affected by a wide range of factors, the values and expectations of those who have power both inside the organisation and externally can exert a strong influence on proposed change strategy. Johnson and Scholes (2002) argue that strategy is a reflection of the attitudes and beliefs of those stakeholders who have most influence on the organisation. Change is also affected by other stakeholders such as the managers and staff, purchasers and suppliers, users of services and their relatives and carers, and the local community. Each of these can influence an organisation and its attempts to change.

Change can be particularly demanding in health and social care services as they operate in a complex environment where legislation, political control, policy imperatives, media attention and many other influences can impact on attempts to change. For example, in the plans to centralise some hospital services – in order to create more viable units with a critical mass of professional expertise – plans can run into opposition from local people who in turn involve politicians and the media with public disquiet used to create opposition to change. This opposition may be helpful in ensuring that the plans are thoroughly tested, but may also ignore evidence that the change would be beneficial to patients and the service.

The concept of stakeholding

The notion of stakeholding developed in the business sector in the 1960s and challenged the traditional view that the responsibility of a company was maximising profits for shareholders. Stakeholder theory sees business comprising a collection of different stakeholders that includes employees, customers, the local community and other interest groups (Linstead *et al*, 2004). This theory was further refined to become an umbrella term to cover individuals and groups whose interests are affected by a company's behaviour. The ethical challenge to business was to find ways to operate that satisfied all stakeholders. The implication of this view is that stakeholders have a legitimate interest in the company, which means it must consider the impact of its actions on them and prioritise actions to meet their needs. This theory suggested that morally a company ought to take wider stakeholder interest into account alongside shareholders in all its activities. It is seen as an ethical corrective to the view that a company's financial interests are the major concern to the exclusion of all other considerations. Strategic change is an arena where stakeholders contest for control of the organisation's attention, resources and outputs.

Although stakeholder theory grew up in the business sector – where it is somewhat more straightforward – it is now central to change in public sector organisations where there are numerous powerful and informed internal and external stakeholders whose views have to be considered when change is proposed. These can include the views of legislators, governing boards, professional staff, the media, opinion leaders and interest groups, often with deeply held opinions and informed views about the activities of an organisation. Effectively managing change in health and social care organisations means understanding the politics surrounding change. Understanding the political dimensions of change can help identify the concerns of stakeholders and what issues need to be considered when planning change.

Stakeholder power

In understanding stakeholder power it is important to recognise that organisations have limited resources, conflicting priorities, unequal power and the formation and dissolution of coalitions with different and changing interests. Using this perspective, organisations are seen as political arenas that contain a complex mix of individual and group interests (Perlmutter & Gummer, 1994). Power is the means by which individuals and groups are able to influence the strategies of an organisation. In most organisations power is shared unequally between various stakeholders. Although the stakeholder perspective tends to complicate managerial decision making – where organisations are effective – senior managers are more likely to employ a political dimension as part of managing change processes such as building coalitions to support change (Heimovics *et al*, 1993).

To understand the political perspective it is important to recognise some important dimensions of organisational life. Bolman and Deal (1991) identify five dimensions:

- organisations are coalitions of varied individuals and interest groups
- individuals have different values, preferences, beliefs, information and perceptions of reality and such differences change slowly, if at all
- most of the important differences in organisations involve the allocation of scarce resources and are decisions about who gets what
- because of scarce resources and enduring differences, conflict is central to organisational dynamics and power is the most important resource
- organisational goals and decisions emerge from bargaining, negotiation and jockeying for position among members of different coalitions.

It is important for managers to understand the political perspective and how in practice organisational strategies are determined following a process of negotiation and bargaining between various internal and external stakeholders. Understanding the relative power of the various stakeholders is critically important in achieving successful change and the methods to adopt, and whether change is successful (Courtney, 2002). Because stakeholder constituencies tend to be complex, managers need to be both politicians and diplomats. This means working with stakeholder groups to establish good relations, developing influencing skills, creating alliances and representing one constituency to each other (Hannigan, 2005).

Stakeholder expectations

Any change in an organisation is likely to have some effect on stakeholders and the relationship between them and the organisation. When change is being planned it is all too easy to become preoccupied with internal processes of change and ignore the impact the change is likely to have on external groups and organisations. Managers can begin the process of implementing change to find that they failed to take account of the views of stakeholders who opposed the change, or resent the lack of consultation, or feel ignored due to poor communication. Upton and Brooks (1995) pose two questions that are important for an organisation to ask itself when it is embarking on change.

1. When an organisation changes, what are likely to be the effects, both positive and negative, on your ability to meet the demands of stakeholders and their perception of the service?

2. What would be the most effective way of responding to the demands of stakeholders, and how can any changes be used to meet this requirement?

The responses you receive from these questions will provide suggestions for the action you need to take in improving your relationship with stakeholders, or reduce any negative consequences of the change. Upton and Brooks suggest that when you are convinced that the proposed changes will improve the service, but stakeholders are still questioning the need for change, it is important that you communicate openly and frankly about why you believe the change is essential and the benefits change will provide. It may not be possible to allay all the fears of all stakeholders, but open and honest communication can reduce some of the resistance to change as it enables stakeholders to feel that their concerns are taken seriously and that they are treated as partners in the change, rather than being ignored or their views dismissed. A dialogue is important as it can provide the opportunity for stakeholders to influence change or suggest options that may improve the changes suggested. This may be time consuming but it has the potential to lead to more satisfactory outcomes than change that is driven by narrow, inward looking solutions which ignore those who are affected by change.

Stakeholder influence

Stakeholders are likely to influence what can be achieved in change, dependent on their power and authority. They judge an organisation's performance according to their own criteria (and not necessarily that of the organisation), and can work with others who share their view to increase their influence on a change strategy. One of the difficulties facing an organisation intending to make major changes is that the more stakeholders that are identified, the more scope there is for the various interests to compete and conflict. Managers who are planning change may be confronted by individuals or groups who may believe, rightly or wrongly, they have a stake in an organisation's future, which may conflict with the views of managers. This dilemma has led to the development of exercises that attempt to distinguish between different stakeholders and their power and interest, both internally and externally.

Smith (1994) suggests that we should treat stakeholders as any individual or group, whether a formal or informal group of individuals, or any institution which both wishes to and is able to affect an organisation's future. They can be split into four broad categories:

- those with direct power over resources, usually associated with formal power to issue directions stemming from a hierarchical relationship

- power of political influence, essentially an indirect power over resources, arising from the ability to influence those who have direct power
- power over production, people on whom the organisation depends to produce the service but who it cannot control without ultimately an element of consent
- power over the environment in which the organisation operates, whether through direct regulation, general legislation or influence on the market place.

In considering a stakeholder's perspective, it is important to have some means of determining the particular weight that should be given to any particular constituency or group of stakeholders. Stakeholder mapping can help you identify expectations and power and is helpful in understanding political priorities. In any analysis of stakeholders it is important to recognise that the identification of potential stakeholders needs to be undertaken in relation to the specific change strategy, as different stakeholder groups will be able to exert power and influence on the particular strategy.

Three stakeholder environments

Another way to understand stakeholders is to visualise the organisation existing within complex network relationships across three environments (Martin & Henderson, 2001). The notion of the three environments can be adapted to represent a series of relationships, for example:

- **the internal environment** – this includes the staff of the organisation who are subject to some managerial control and influence
- **the near environment** – this includes service users, carers, contractors and suppliers who cannot be controlled, but can be influenced
- **the far environment** – this includes those organisations and individuals that have power and influence, for example national politicians and policy makers. Although it may be difficult to influence these players, organisations can respond to changes in the far environment in order to manage the potential impact on them.

What this notion of the three environments offers is a way of understanding the context in which stakeholder power and influence operate and the extent to which an organisation is able to manage and influence different stakeholder constituencies.

Identifying and mapping stakeholders

Bryson (2004) suggests that stakeholder analysis is one of the most important things an organisation embarking on change should attend to because stakeholders are critical to success. Furthermore, he states that if an organisation does not know who its stakeholders are, it has no criteria to judge the organisation and how it is performing against that criteria and cannot be clear about what it should be doing to satisfy its key stakeholders. The first stage is to identify your organisation's stakeholders and completing this exercise will give a more accurate picture of this stakeholder constituency.

The power/interest matrix

A well established technique for identifying stakeholders and their power and interest is the power/interest matrix that classifies stakeholders in relation to the power they hold and the extent to which they are likely to show interest in an organisation's strategies (Mendelow, 1991). The power/interest matrix is used to assess the power and interest of stakeholders identified in the mapping exercise and enables you to classify them in relation to the power they hold and the extent to which they are likely to show interest in supporting or opposing a particular strategy. The outcome of the analysis can then be used to indicate the type of relationship the organisation wishes to establish with the stakeholder groups in the different quadrants of the matrix.

Figure 8.1: Stakeholder mapping: the power/interest matrix

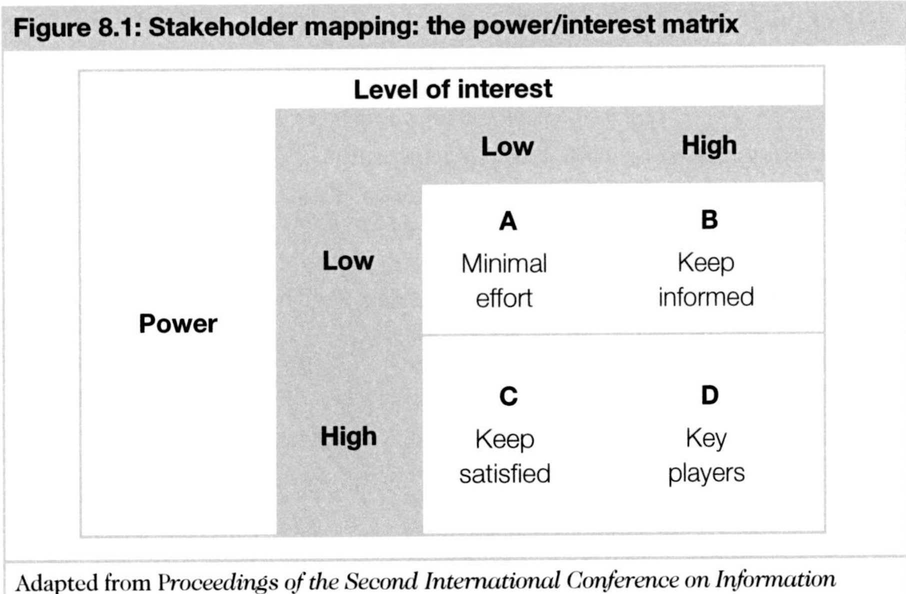

Adapted from *Proceedings of the Second International Conference on Information Systems* © A Mendelow (1991) Cambridge, MA.

This matrix enables you to identify the stakeholders who have an expectation of your organisation and who may attempt to influence the proposed change. The 2x2 matrix has four quadrants which represent the stakeholders' power and influence in relation to the organisation and the type of relationship which you may need to establish with the different stakeholders identified. One dimension represents degrees of power and the other represents levels of interest. Taking each quadrant in turn, map the stakeholders you have identified in terms of their power and influence.

- **Quadrant D:** these are the key stakeholders and they are of high importance. They will be critical to the success of your proposed change.
- **Quadrant C:** these stakeholders may be powerful in relation to the change, but are not necessarily active. It is nevertheless important to ensure that they are not underrated or neglected, and then move in opposition to the change.
- **Quadrant B:** this group of stakeholders may be relatively powerless, but if ignored can influence the attitude of more powerful stakeholders.
- **Quadrant A:** these stakeholders are relatively unimportant to the organisation as they have little power or influence and general information on the proposed change and its benefits may be sufficient.

Johnson and Scholes (2002) offer useful advice on managing the stakeholder relationship. They suggest that stakeholder mapping offers a number of opportunities. It can:

- show who is likely to block and facilitate change, and how you need to respond, for example, through education or persuasion
- show whether it is necessary to work with some stakeholders to reposition them, either lessening the influence of some key players or identifying other more potential key players to champion the change
- ensure that some stakeholders are supported to maintain their level of interest or power, or others discouraged from repositioning themselves.

What these activities raise, according to Johnson and Scholes (2002), are important questions about the role of senior managers and others in change teams, and the extent to which they are involved in political activities surrounding change. Do they act as honest brokers, balancing the views of different stakeholders, or are they answerable to powerful stakeholders such as politicians, trustees or non-executives? Or do they work 'behind the throne' to construct strategies to suit their own purposes, managing stakeholder expectations to ensure acceptance of these strategies? Johnson and Scholes see these as important issues that will be determined by the governance arrangements in an organisation and the ethical stance of the organisation and its individual managers. This could lead to some stakeholders feeling they have been manipulated to ensure that the managers' preferred options are successful, in spite of the strong feelings of opposition from users of services. Managers may face loud opposing claims from various interests and will quickly encounter the problem of how 'balance' should be defined and recognised between different groups and interests.

Case study

Stakeholder influence

Following a major public consultation exercise, a primary care trust (PCT) proposed a series of changes which involved the re-configuration of the accident and emergency services (A&E) departments in three general hospitals. This proposed change recognised that increasingly the majority of treatment provided was undertaken outside hospitals and that services needed to evolve to ensure that where complex treatment was needed, it was provided in centres that had access to sufficient clinical expertise. These changes would involve the development of a major general hospital (MGH) which would provide an enhanced level of provision, and local general hospitals (LGH) which would offer a more limited service for those with lesser needs. The intention was to retain A&E services at all three hospitals, but develop a general hospital with a more extensive range of services where facilities and expertise would be concentrated to provide a wider level of service.

Following the publication of the PCT's options for re-configuring the services, a considerable level of opposition emerged from a wide range of stakeholders, including clinicians, local councillors, MPs and campaign groups. The plans caused such concern to councillors and MPs from the constituencies affected that they protested to the Secretary of State. They questioned the wisdom of the proposed changes and the quality of evidence provided by the PCT, specifically the proposed service model, the conflicting clinical opinion and the status of local hospitals, which in the case of the LGHs would have their facilities downgraded. The local campaign groups rejected changes to hospitals in their localities and used the media to generate considerable opposition to the proposals, organising marches and rallies and online petitions. The local campaign group also used statements from clinicians opposed to the changes to highlight the potential dangers if the changes went ahead.

The following stakeholder analysis of the changes demonstrates the potential of powerful stakeholders to influence decisions, and the mobilisation of local interest groups to quickly form and using the power of the media to generate powerful opposition to change.

		Level of interest	
		Low	**High**
Power	**Low**	**Box A** **Minimal effort** ▶ Potential users of services	**Box B** **Keep informed** ▶ GPs ▶ Staff in affected departments ▶ Campaign groups ▶ Local media (newspapers, TV and radio)
	High	**Box C** **Keep satisfied** ▶ Local politicians (scrutiny committee) ▶ Patients representation panel	**Box D** **Key players** ▶ PCT ▶ MPs ▶ A&E consultants ▶ Chair of options appraisal panel

Comment

What this case study demonstrates is the power of stakeholders to influence decision-making. No matter how much the plans for reconfiguration are based on well researched evidence, they can be undermined by the power of local interest groups who in turn use the media and national celebrities to publicise their cause. It also points to the difficulty in making any changes to services, no matter how necessary, where vested interests are able to mobilise opposition, or where politicians conscious of local opinion support opposition to change.

This case study reinforces Scholes' (2001) view that where there is both support and opposition among key players (Box D), this becomes a 'political battleground' and can freeze commitment and decision-making. A second scenario is where there are numerous opponents of the strategy (Box B) who have little power and are disregarded and consequently incited to gain power though building alliances or lobbying other stakeholders in Box C and D. A situation Scholes describes as a 'political time bomb'. Both these scenarios were present in the case study.

In their research of the change processes in the reconfiguration of hospital services, Fulop *et al* (2008) have identified the way that different stakeholders, with different interests, can play a significant role in the reconfiguration process. Where the downgrading of a hospital is considered (as in the case study), it is likely to produce major political conflict. They also identify class and geography as being important. Smaller towns with large middle class populations are more likely to produce conflict between the public and health service planners on reconfiguration (as in this case study). The authors also warn that planners can assume that reconfiguration is a technocratic process where evidence is sufficient to convince stakeholders of the value of change. This can result in their failing to understand how services are perceived by the public and the notion of public entitlement and trust in the NHS, which plays a significant role.

Putting yourself in the stakeholders' shoes

Upton and Brooks (1995) suggest a useful exercise that can be used to prepare for change. It involves rehearsing the demands of stakeholders and can be a helpful exercise in testing the impact of meeting their needs or ignoring them. This means that you ask yourself as accurately as possible what their demands are likely to be and how your organisation is currently responding. For example:

A group of disabled people: '*We want to know when you are going to provide us with personal budgets so that we can make our own decisions about the services we want to support us?*'

A director of adult care services: '*We are having to make a number of changes in our procedures to accommodate the new arrangements for individual budgets, and we have started training social workers in using the new assessment forms and can't guarantee we will be able to assess all service users in the next six months.*'

Upton and Brooks see this exercise as an effective way of creating a readiness for change, with change teams forced to adopt an external viewpoint and position. It means putting yourself in the shoes of others and seeing the demands from their perspective. It can also be useful in revealing the tensions and conflicts between the demands of different stakeholders and the compromises that may have to be reached if you are to satisfy as many stakeholders' interests as possible. It can lead to an organisation having to reposition itself to meet the demands of stakeholders.

Learning the views of stakeholders

One area that is often neglected in change is a genuine attempt to listen to what the people who use a service actually value and what they want to see improved. It is particularly important that managers listen to what service users want and how they view the services they receive. Managers and professionals may identify what they believe is needed that may not accord with the views of service users. The evidence from service users of what they value is graphically described in the *Shaping Our Lives* publications, where a user-led organisation has carried out its own research and provides professionals with a valuable insight into how people who use services actually view them (Beresford, 2005).

In the accounts of service users, concern was raised about their involvement in consultation and what these actually achieved. They were sceptical about 'user involvement', and experienced 'involvement fatigue' due to too many initiatives and saw consultation as tokenistic at best (see www.shapingourlives.org.uk). Consultation exercises were seen as window dressing or sham democracy, with decisions already taken and consultation used to demonstrate that an organisation had been listening to the voice of the user. All attempts at consultation run the risk that those responding to requests for feedback on change plans believe that decisions have already been taken.

Another risk is that consultation can use language or techniques that alienate or patronise users who do not feel engaged and decide not to respond. For example, questionnaires that are written in a way that make it difficult for users to respond, or where there is use of jargon that excludes those who are not party to 'management speak'.

When deciding to make changes in services it is important to understand how stakeholders view the current service and where improvements are needed. Where there are well established groups with explicit expectations about the service, it is easier to ascertain their wishes. Other stakeholders who are not part of established groups may find it more difficult to articulate their views and for these stakeholders other means have to be found to understand their views. The risk with collecting the views of established groups and a small sample of those who are moved to respond may result in a self-selected and skewed sample. Wheeler and Grice (2000) describe a range of methods that can be used to identify the wishes of individuals and groups, including:

- **suggestion boxes** strategically placed to allow service users to make comments and suggestions; these have advantages if they are accessible, such as in waiting rooms, and where they can be used with anonymity and not observed by staff; responses tend to be self-selected, but the bias is reduced if the box is easy to use with a correspondingly higher response rate
- **questionnaires** used before and after interventions offer the service users, carers and relatives the opportunity to comment on the service and whether it met their needs, and if not, what improvements would have helped; here the decision is whether to use closed questions that give quantitative information which is easy to collate and draw conclusions, or open questions which offer more opportunity to explore issues with users and carers, at the risk that the responses are difficult to generalise to the whole population of individuals using the service; a combination of the two approaches can maximise information
- **interviews**, particularly those administered before, during or after treatment, have the advantage of a high response; again, as in questionnaires, closed or open questions can be used with a series of closed questions followed by open questions generating useful data; Wheeler and Grice caution that interviews can be an expensive exercise and need to be used sparingly.
- **focus groups** are used when researchers want to learn about the views of those using a service and where bringing a group of stakeholders together in a group setting provides a free ranging discussion about a service; it

is important that the focus group is a representative sample of people using the service and that the facilitation ensures confidentiality, thereby encouraging openness and honesty about the issues discussed. Wheeler and Grice argue that focus groups have advantages over questionnaires and interviews in that they encourage participants to offer more considered views after discussion and negotiation with others in the group.

Summary

This chapter has described the importance of understanding the concept of stakeholding which is critical in planning change, particularly of a strategic nature. Ignoring the power and influence of stakeholders can result in the most thorough plans being undermined or blocked through a neglect of stakeholder views. The difficulty for managers in health and social care organisations is the potential wide range of stakeholders likely to be interested in any change that impacts on services where they have an interest. This includes both internal stakeholders, who may be powerful professionals who are unconvinced by management-led changes, and external stakeholders who can quickly form strong opposition to change if well organised and make effective use of the media to support their opposition to change. When faced with the complexity of stakeholder interests it is essential that you are familiar with the wide range of techniques that can assist in identifying stakeholders, and adopting their perspectives to understand more fully both support and opposition to proposed change strategies. It is also important to learn about stakeholders' views and the chapter has offered a series of suggestions for understanding more fully how stakeholders view the services they use. Taken together, these activities can enable managers to plan change more effectively with greater potential for success than where stakeholders are ignored or underestimated.

References

Beresford P (2005) What services users want. *The Guardian*, 23 March.

Bolman LG & Deal TE (1991) *Reframing Organizations: Artistry, choice and leadership*. San Francisco: Jossey-Bass.

Bryson JM (2004) *Strategic Planning for Public and Nonprofit Organizations: A guide to strengthening and sustaining organizational achievement*. San Francisco: Jossey-Bass.

Courtney R (2002) *Strategic Management for Voluntary and Nonprofit Organizations*. London: Routledge.

Fulop NP & Spurgeon P (2008) Processes of change in the reconfiguration of hospital services: The role of stakeholder involvement. In: L McKee, E Ferlie & P Hyde (Eds) *Organizing and Reorganizing: Power and change in health service organisations*. Basingstoke: Palgrave Macmillan.

Hannigan T (2005) *Management: Concepts and practices* (4th edition). Harlow: FT Prentice Hall.

Heimovics RD, Herman RD & Jurkiewicz CL (1993) Executive leadership and resource dependence in nonprofit organizations: a frame analysis. *Public Administration Review* **53** (5) 419–427.

Johnson G & Scholes K (2002) *Exploring Corporate Strategy: Text and cases* (6th edition). Harlow: Pearson Education.

Linstead S, Fulop L & Lilley S (2004) *Management and Organization: A critical text*. Basingstoke: Palgrave MacMillan.

Martin V & Henderson E (2001) *Managing in Health and Social Care*. London: Routledge.

Mendelow A (1991) *Proceedings of the Second International Conference on Information Systems*, Cambridge, MA.

Perlmutter FD & Gummer B (1994) Managing organizational transitions. In: RD Harman (Ed) *The Jossey-Bass Handbook of Nonprofit Leadership and Management*. San Francisco: Jossey-Bass.

Scholes K (2001) Stakeholder mapping: a practical tool for public sector managers. In: Johnson G & Scholes K (Eds) *Exploring Public Sector Strategy*. Harlow: Pearson Education.

Smith RJ (1994) *Strategic Management and Planning in the Public Sector*. Harlow: Longman.

Upton T & Brooks B (1995) *Managing Change in the NHS*. Buckingham: Open University Press.

Wheeler D & Grice N (2000) *Management in Health Care*. Cheltenham: Stanley Thornes Publishers.

Section 3:

Inter-professional issues and innovation

Chapter 9

Inter-professional collaboration for change

By Janet McCray

Key points

- The transformation of service delivery models
- Definitions of collaborative practice
- Examples of changes in service delivery
- Leadership actions

Introduction

This chapter will begin by offering definitions of inter-professional collaboration and continue to provide an overview of the service delivery developments which underpin it. A review of research into elements of collaborative practice will help you understand some workers' responses to uncertainty. Techniques for achieving successful change through team work are presented and involve reflecting on professional roles, inter-professional learning and inter-professional theory while using active team leading and working strategies. Inter-professional collaboration as part of the change process requires an understanding of the critical success factors needed. Additionally, a grasp of the challenges faced by leaders and managers of teams when things don't go well and strategies to understand and overcome these is also required. The chapter will offer a series of points that you can use when leading and managing change in inter-professional contexts.

Transformation of service delivery

Service delivery models in health and social care are undergoing major transformation. Inter-professional practice – where professionals from different disciplines work together to achieve the same goals for the client, patient or service user – is one of the main vehicles for creating, implementing and sustaining change in and across organisational structures. An acknowledgement of fragmented service design and a need to create a more seamless service for people and their families have built this foundation for change. However, change is not always straightforward and people may bring to it a number of previous experiences and a set of expectations about their role, position and status.

When inter-professional collaboration is involved, status, ideology and the legitimisation of differing groups and agencies are at issue, and in challenging economic times they all play a factor in the success and sustainability of change. Emphasis on inter-professional working has resulted in new and different approaches to collaborative practice by professional groups and has impacted on the everyday practice of professionals. This has resulted in some very exciting solutions to complex problems and cases, yet at the same time critics of inter-professional practice have challenged its effectiveness and impact on the lives of service users and carers.

Definitions of collaborative practice

In talking about collaboration and its components, it is important to begin with some definitions. The World Health Organization (2010) observes that:

'Collaborative practice in health care occurs when multiple health workers from different professional backgrounds provide comprehensive services by working with patients, their families, carers and communities to deliver the highest quality of care across settings.'

Collaborative working often forms an element of inter-professional, multi-professional or multi-agency team work and terms such as 'inter-professional' and 'multidisciplinary' are often used to mean the same thing. What is also important is that vocationally qualified workers are included within the professional groupings. Multi-professional practice involves practice with a number of professionals from different areas or sectors. This means that professional groups may agree with a family or patient on an intervention, but each professional group will work separately, not together, to provide the care agreed. Inter-professional practice where professionals work across boundaries to support service users may be more effective.

Sheehan *et al* (2007) offer a further three definitions:

- **multidisciplinary** – where interaction and communication across teams can be informal and people remain in their own professional role
- **interdisciplinary** – were the roles of professionals overlap and communication is formal and informal for the good of the service user, who should be at the centre of the focus of intervention
- **transdisciplinary** – where there is greater overlap, blending and blurring of professional roles and people may be employed in roles or activities which are based on skill or expertise to work towards change.

Present and future challenges: examples of changes in service delivery

The global and subsequent national embrace of new public management has been influential in the design and implementation of policy frameworks, which require changing models of professional and inter-professional practice. New public management has been a response to concern about traditional public sector administration, in relation to:

- being economic, effective and efficient
- the over dominance of professionals
- the size of the public sector and its bureaucratic practice
- a belief in more skilful management of services in the private sector.

Drivers for change in service delivery are taking place in this complex and often contested context. Such developments require professionals to change their practice, team memberships and roles in order to network, engage and deliver performance targets, which may have previously not been viewed as part of their remit. These actions are occurring when new ways of working with service users are expected. Furthermore, these new partnerships across communities, agencies and professionals in the public, private and third sector mean that service models and networks are in transition and a number of new challenges are emerging to confront the leader of an inter-professional team.

Challenges to leaders of inter-professional teams

Protecting people at risk

The need to ensure a more effective safety net for the protection of vulnerable people in society, notably children vulnerable to abuse but also the protection of adults, means that new frameworks have been put in place. For example, the Common Assessment Framework (CAF) which is centred on preventative action to ensure children and families receive support and changes are made at an early stage of need. Such drivers require professionals to work very differently and create new configurations and responsibilities underpinning professional practice. Collins (2010) notes that the concept of the lead professional in the CAF means that professionals with vocational qualifications may be leading processes moving away from traditional professional structures and responses.

In Hean *et al*'s research (2006), the origins of views about the professional practice of health care professionals came from very early professional experiences – thus a leader should not take agreement as a given in collaborative teamwork. Clear frameworks and processes are needed from the outset to enable the cohesion of team members and create the right environment for the team to develop. This means deciding on accountability and responsibility at the start of projects and offering reminders and updates throughout a project's lifespan. Hean *et al* found that multi-agency work may often flounder and inhibit change because of over complicated structures, and they note that leaders should place energy on process and outcomes. Equally, it is important to be clear about the amount of financial or other resources to be contributed by a partner agency and recognise that this might change because of restraints.

Exploring feelings about change in the inter-professional context

Just as support is required to explore tensions around roles in the collaborative work setting in ordinary circumstances, during periods of change and uncertainty it becomes even more vital. In inter-professional literature some interesting insights into professional practice may help in terms of assumptions about professionals' capacity to deal with change.

Lingard *et al* (2003) explore the role of uncertainty in patient case presentation by student doctors. Their paper explores the progression from the student role to the professional role as the participants learn to manage aspects of uncertainty. These aspects are all clinical and related to their professional sphere. Lingard *et al*'s study indicated that the outcomes of change impacted on their professional socialisation. Here, what is interesting when transformative practice is discussed is that uncertainty may have a significant emotional impact on this group of professionals. The uncertainty is related to the management of their clinical practice and so highly socialised processes may be challenged, and hence previously learnt behavioural repertoires are not available, thus creating stresses around identity.

In social work practice Ellermann (1998) explored the impact of alternative discourses in practice such as feminist and black perspectives. Her research found that moving from a dominant but familiar patriarchal Eurocentric model created uncertainty for social workers. Ellermann suggests this position challenges the professional's sense of self, creating a lack of openness in their communication with others. These studies from medicine and social work may begin to explain some of the responses to change and uncertainty that are presented when inter-professional collaboration is required, and setting this within a broader context of service delivery uncertainty means that there may be unexpected barriers to public sector change.

Leadership action in response to challenges to inter-professional teams

In practice, power and authority may lie in different places and where previously professional leaders managed their own profession group, different models of leadership may come to exist when change has taken place.

As a leader you may need to take into account:

- the loss of security that professionals may feel as traditional roles, boundaries and management structures are no longer in place
- that language, terminology, working practices and values will be different
- the need to work towards clarity of terms and actions with your team
- any assumptions you may have that people want the same outcomes and agree on ways forward; these may need to be explored and clarified.

Moves towards personalised care

New models of commissioning services underpinned by personalisation mean that service users and the third sector will play a major part in service design and delivery. Carr and Dittrich (2008) define personalisation in adult services as:

'...finding new collaborative ways of working and developing local partnerships, which produce a range of services for people to choose from and opportunities for social inclusion, tailoring support to people's individual needs.'

As the care of elderly people has moved to the community, local authorities are increasingly working in formal partnerships with third sector services who are commissioned to manage and deliver social care support to older people living at home. Due to this, different ways of working and communicating will be required and collaboration will involve working across organisations in health and social care. The management of the expectations of stakeholders and what is possible will be critical in the challenging economic context of service cuts across all sectors.

Team membership and collaboration will work on a number of levels with both permanent and temporary team members, some of whom will be service users and carers. Research from Hudson (2007) notes the characteristics of pessimistic and optimistic teams. Pessimistic teams include a distinctiveness of trait, knowledge, power, accountability and culture, in contrast to the optimistic model where team members share a commonality of values, accountability, learning, location, culture and care.

If change, inclusivity and transformative practice are to occur, then the optimistic team model is best placed to be proactive and responsive. To get there, team members will need support to gain an understanding of new ways of working and what they entail. As a leader you should be aware of need versus resource-driven services which may be both unifying and divisive, resulting in a challenge of role shift for everyone. You should watch out for any wane of enthusiasm as access to scarce resources is rationed and when a return on investment might not be immediately clear. Some team members may need support and supervision to see the value of this level of investment. The economic climate will also have an impact. Tensions around role boundaries and territory may emerge during change processes and leadership strategies will need careful planning and attention.

Commonly, responses to changing patterns of service delivery, such as personalisation, are based on organisational restructures and professional boundary changes. Many research and practice based solutions for change require agreement and common goals from all participants. For the transformation of services and to help professionals learn and develop, dealing with conflict and contradiction may be necessary constants to enable creative solutions.

Exploring well-being and job satisfaction in changing inter-professional practice

The nature and purpose of teams may also impact on performance and levels of inter-professional well-being. Change has resulted in less geographically located teams and more dependence on contact through information systems. Equally, the purpose of some teams means that their establishment is only temporary and longevity is finite. Saunders and Ahuja (2006) explore characteristics of teams in business settings. They note that the likely behaviours of people and their investment in interaction in teams may be dependent on their anticipation of likely future working. In contrast, longer term projects and teamwork have other influencing factors, such as seeking effective ways of working.

In more geographically distant or virtual team working, Saunders and Ahuja (2006) observe that the support offered to members and the investment in the interpersonal relationship may vary, particularly on short-term projects. This has implications for job satisfaction among temporary team members. Lack of face-to-face interaction means that the usual positive corridor catch up or social exchange is missing, and Saunders and Ahuja note that informal contact like this contributes to group identity and team member identification. This absence means that workers are required to create multiple and sometimes conflicting identities. Saunders and Ahuja note that this can create conflicting loyalties for individuals who work across organisations. Ultimately, it can impact on job satisfaction and sticking with what's known rather than endorsing change.

Leadership action in transition to personalised services

Leaders will need to engage and motivate staff and partners to work effectively in their inter-professional contexts so that the transition from service-centred to individual-centred support can take hold. This means that as leaders support their team to undertake new roles and responses and review how these roles are valued by others in the team, including service users and carers, planned leadership strategies will be vital.

Leaders will need to recognise:

- the importance of scheduling time for people to develop and learn new skills, to assist them to reflect on their performance in the team
- evaluation of success and failure and be clear about what this looks like and how it is measured
- methods and models of communication, and how these should be reviewed
- how much models of communication could impact on team roles and on leadership strategy
- that the mix of professionals and potential agendas can create conflict
- the need to work with your team to determine models of practice to be used when dealing with conflict
- how the team's emotional resilience may need attention; this means determining how well the team copes in adverse conditions and when to plan and deliver support to the team members (and this is not just about workload management or performance measurement)
- what a model of good teamwork practice and collaboration looks like
- the purpose of regular debriefing groups with the team when things work well and when also they don't
- that it may be helpful to use peer learning as part of collaboration in difficult situations.

Transforming support through the reconfiguration of services and technology

Rapidly developing technological changes in operating practice in acute care and the home based management of post-operative conditions has made the journey from secondary health care to primary health care much shorter. However, these changes mean that work is planned and delivered across organisational boundaries, which can be fragile and need complex management to maintain and to understand their impact on practice. These factors may cause role conflict in inter-professional working and create confusion around individual and team identity. These operate and play out with professional and inter-professional differences about approaches to the perceived management and support of the service user or carer, and issues linked to power, status and authority which are in operation in particular organisations and contexts.

A theoretical approach which may help in understanding these dynamics is activity theory. Activity theory focuses on conflict and how it works in organisations and attempts to explain this within a time of change in services. It is concerned with what happens (processes and communication) in inter-professional practice and how we learn to work together (Hean *et al*, 2006). Warmington *et al* (2004) use activity theory to explore beyond traditional models and concerns of inter-professional working. It offers a different point of connection which they call the 'object' – that is the vehicle or the 'what' of inter-professional practice. The essential premise is not a concern with bureaucratic structures and rigid professional roles, but with processes that are more fluid which they define as 'knotworking'. Warmington *et al* (2004) write:

'Engeström's (1995) notions of boundary crossing suggest that new developments in learning for interagency working should focus upon the potential spaces for renegotiation of professional practice that are opened up.'

It is getting to this point and beyond which will be required for inter-professional practice within temporary and constantly changing practice settings. The World Health Organization notes that for successful collaborative practice '*reflecting critically on one's own relationship within a team and transferring inter-professional learning to the work setting*' (WHO, 2010) are important aspects of practice for all.

The team leader can work with the team to explore beyond what seems like the straightforward task or goal oriented learning activity to examine other aspects of collaboration. Newell Jones and Lord (2008) adapt Illeris's tension triangle (Illeris, 2002) to explore inter-professional learning. Illeris suggests that learning has three aspects (See Figure 9.1 on p.158). First, knowledge that is cognitive. Second, psychodynamic learning connected to emotion and motivation, and societal learning related to communication and interaction. When teams are exploring new ways of working and changing practice, professional identities and boundaries may, as Newell Jones and Lord (2008) note, become challenged and lead to emotional responses by team members. This can lead to a negative outcome if not addressed and members are unsupported and subsequently not engaged to explore tensions. From this position inter-professional team leadership must facilitate new learning for professionals.

Figure 9.1: Tension triangle

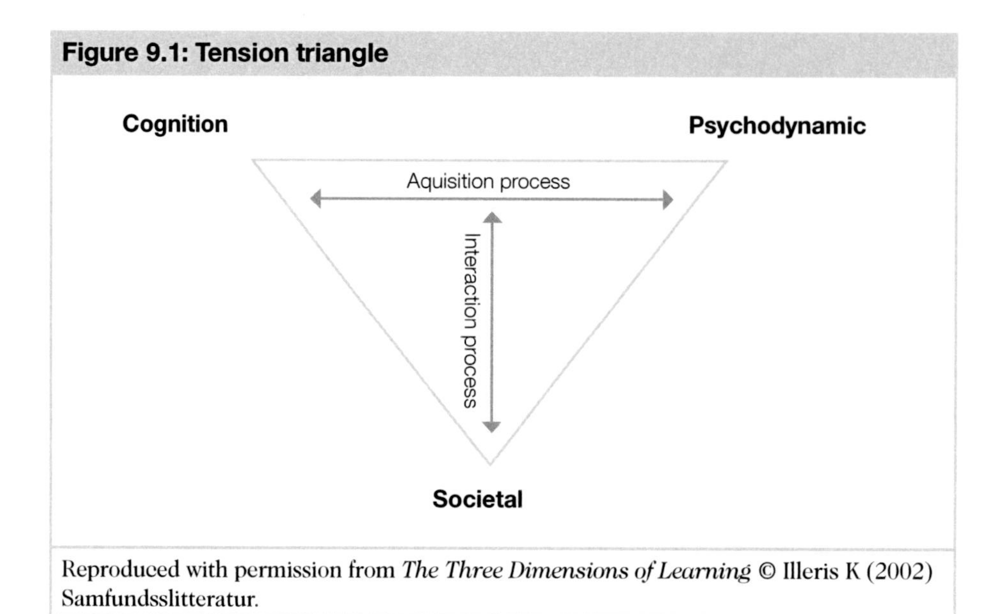

Reproduced with permission from *The Three Dimensions of Learning* © Illeris K (2002) Samfundsslitteratur.

Leadership action on supporting flexibility and creativity

It is important for the leader and organisation to reflect on how they support practitioner flexibility and creativity around inter-agency working and collaboration. A key role of the leader of change will be:

- to ensure that team members acquire new learning and skills to ensure outcomes are met for service users and their families
- checking what form of professional updating, for example around IT systems and project management, is needed as identified and measured through effective performance management
- helping the team to explore the tensions between rules, tools, objects (the what) of practice and professional identity (Daniels *et al*, 2007).

Case study

Action working sets and collaborative working

A learning disability partnership board was anxious to ensure that the priorities from *Valuing People Now* (DH, 2009) were agreed upon and an integrated service delivery plan was put in place. While good progress had been made, the current economic climate meant that some tough decisions were going to be needed. Collaboration across agencies and partner stakeholders was going to be vital for the right changes to be put in place, and yet this way of working was limited in some areas.

Leaders in the service thought different approaches were required for change to be lasting. They decided to invite key stakeholders to participate in a year-long action learning set project. Action learning sets usually include six people who wish to work together through a challenge or urgent problem. The set is facilitated by an experienced coach who will enable the group to get to an agreed response or strategy. The action learning set approach would be different from an agreement by a committee with a subsequent mixed response and commitment to agreed outcomes depending on stakeholders' feelings about the proposed activity. Instead they felt that action learning sets would help facilitate the change process as they enabled stakeholder members to do three important things:

- agree on their leadership strategy to make the goals agreed happen – in this case the priorities that were set
- members would work on their feelings around these changes in service delivery through reflection and questioning
- through supporting each other, challenging leadership activity and getting more effective as a group, the set could work after the project had finished ensuring change was evaluated and sustained.

Comment

The partnership board found that the action learning set approach helped in a number of ways. It prevented silo working and provided a safe place for conflict to be aired about different priorities by members. Because of commitment to the set, a rollout plan for priorities was gained by all. Members worked hard to agree their part in making the priorities happen, and were accountable to the other members of the set so change took place. When things were tough, set members had support from other members and were able to discuss strategies for change and their potential consequences. Finally, as the set worked so well, members wanted to continue to meet after the project had finished to sustain and evaluate the changes that were put in place.

Summary

This chapter has offered a series of definitions of collaborative practice which clarify some of the confusion around what collaborative working actually means. You will have seen that collaborative multiagency working requires leaders working in collaborative settings to understand and put into practice strategies for driving and delivering change. Different approaches to support understanding and engaging of stakeholders and the underpinning knowledge to create change in the collaborative context are needed. Working in such challenging circumstances across boundaries means that leading change is not always easy. A leader requires a number of essential skills, knowledge and understanding to manage change. By gaining these qualities leaders should feel empowered and equipped to lead and support others towards successful inter-professional change.

References

Carr S & Dittrich R (2008) *Personalisation: A rough guide* (Report 20). London: SCIE.

Collins F (2010) *Cultures, Identities: Interprofessional collaborative working and conceptualizations of practice*. Unpublished Mphil/Phd thesis (in progress). Department of Social Sciences: University of Chichester.

Daniels H, Leadbetter B, Warmington P, Edwards A, Martin D, Popova A, Apostolov A, Middleton D & Brown S (2007) Learning in and for multi-agency working. Oxford *Review of Education* **33** (4) 521–538.

Department of Health (2009) *Valuing People Now*. London: Department of Health.

Ellermann A (1998) Can discourse analysis enable reflective social work practice? *Social Work Education* **17** (1) 35–44.

Engeström R (1995) Voice as communicative action. *Mind, Culture, and Activity* **2** 192–214.

Hean S, Macleod Clark J, Adams K & Humphris D (2006) Will opposites attract? Similarities and difference in students' perceptions of the stereotype profiles of other health and social care professional groups. *Journal of Interprofessional Care* **20** (2) 162–181.

Hudson B (2007) The Sedgfield Integrated Team. *Journal of Interprofessional Care* **21** (1).

Illeris K (2002) *The Three Dimensions of Learning*. Frederiksberg: Samfundslitteratur.

Lingard L, Garwood K, Schryerb CF & Spafford MM (2003) A certain art of uncertainty: case presentation and the development of professional. *Identity Social Science and Medicine* **56** (3) 603–613.

Newell Jones K & Lord M (2008) A learning and teaching framework for inter-professional learning. In: E Howkins & J Bray (Eds) *Preparing for Interprofessional Teaching*. Oxford: John Radcliffe.

Saunders CS & Ahuja MK (2006) Are all distributed teams the same? *Small Group Research* **37**(6) 662–700.

Sheehan D, Robertson L & Ormond T (2007) Comparison of language used and patterns of communication in inter-professional and multidisciplinary teams. *Journal of Interprofessional Care* **21**(1) 17–30.

Warmington P, Daniels H, Edwards A, Brown S, Leadbetter J, Martin D & Middleton D (2004) *Interagency Collaboration: A review of the literature*. Bath: Learning in and for Interagency Working Project, University of Bath.

World Health Organization (2010) *Framework for Action on Interprofessional Education & Collaborative Practice*. Geneva: World Health Organization.

Chapter 10

Supporting innovation and change

Key points

- Definitions and types of innovation
- Individual responses to innovation
- Factors in the innovation–decision process
- Individual and organisational support for innovation
- Creating conditions that support innovation

Introduction

Health and social care services face a number of critical challenges, including reducing the current levels of variability in the provision of services and improving performance to equate with the best performing organisations. These services are also experiencing increasing demand on the part of users who want services to be designed around their expectations and requirements. The additional pressure of severe funding constraints that now face services will require new and innovative ways of delivering high quality services with reduced levels of resources. Introducing innovations, such as new practices or procedures, are complex and dependent on a wide range of factors at both individual and organisational levels. Organisational factors can in turn play a significant role in the potential reception and spread of innovations. This chapter will examine what is meant by innovations, how they are received and spread, and which individual and organisational factors are important to consider when understanding how innovations are adopted and diffused.

What is innovation?

An innovation is an idea, practice or product that is perceived as being new by an individual, group or organisation. Rogers (2003) suggests that it is less important that the idea or practice is objectively new, but rather that it is the perceived newness of the idea for the individual that determines their reaction to it. If the idea seems new to the individual then it is an innovation. Johnson and Williams (2007) describe innovation as the '*process whereby creative thought develops into something tangible, and creative people are those who generate ideas, whereas the innovative process means taking those ideas and applying them in a practical application that is needed or desired by the organisation*'.

A more specific definition describes innovation as: '*novel changes in a system, which are performed and achieved for the first time in its development. The innovation provides a better solution to a problem from the previous state. The decisive determinant of the innovative content of the new solution is its relation to the old one. It is the relation to previous solutions and approaches that determine the degree of innovation of a novel change*' (GB Equal Support Unit, 2006).

Mulgan and Albury (2003), in their paper on introducing successful innovation in the public sector, state that innovation is '*the creation and implementation of new processes, products, services and methods of delivery which result in significant improvements in outcomes, efficiency, effectiveness and quality. They describe innovation as a core activity of the public sector critical to the future of health and social care services, with innovation seen as core activity that can help the sector improve performance and increase public value, and respond to the expectations of service users. It can also help in increasing efficiency and reducing costs*'.

Innovation is not synonymous with change as ongoing change is a feature of all organisations (Halvorsen *et al*, 2005). For example, a change takes place when an organisation recruits a new member of staff to undertake routine practices, whereas an innovation takes place when the organisation recruits a member of staff in order to import new knowledge and practice in a way that is novel in the organisation. Innovation also differs from ongoing change in that it introduces the notion of a completely different way of working that can radically change how individuals see their work and can lead to fundamental adaptations in the systems and processes of service delivery.

Types of innovation

Innovations can take a number of forms, including strategic or policy level changes where new organisations, missions, strategies and goals are introduced; for example, the introduction of NHS Direct. Innovations can introduce changes in the design of services as seen in a shift towards providing housing rather than residential care under *Supporting People* developments. They can include new or altered ways of delivering services and interacting with service users, seen in providing users with personal budgets to purchase and control their own services. Innovations can include changes in organisational forms as services reduce their hierarchies in order to create more responsive services. Lastly, they can include new or improved ways of interacting with other systems and professionals through the integration of health and social care professionals in multidisciplinary teams.

Innovations can range from the incremental, through the radical and the transformative, according to Mulgan and Albury (2003).

- **Incremental:** where there are frequent small scale changes to existing services or processes that are common to all organisations, but often pass unnoticed. They tend to change specific services, rather than a radical change to the structure and processes of an organisation, but they are the necessary drivers in the pursuit of improvement in public services.
- **Radical:** these occur less frequently and are new services or 'ways of doing things' that are developed, or where new ways of organising and delivering services are established.
- **Transformative:** these are rare innovations that give rise to new workforce structures and new types of organisation. They transform entire sectors and dramatically change the relationship between organisations. These innovations can take long time periods to have their full effect and may require fundamental changes in organisational, social and cultural arrangements.

Case study

Radical innovation

The growing support for the policy of personalisation is an example of a radical innovation that will involve new ways of organising and delivering services. This policy is intended to give individuals greater choice and control over the arrangements made for their support. Typically, the person needing support is allocated a personal budget following an assessment of their need. They will control (or have it controlled for them by someone they nominate) and decide how they use the money to purchase support that meets their needs. In their report on self-directed services, Leadbeater *et al* (2008) described four factors that have come together to spur innovation. These are:

1. the view that current social care services are failing to deliver the personalised services people want, and are poor value for money
2. that current approaches to the delivery of social care has created a political environment favourable to innovation as seen in *Putting People First* (DH, 2007)
3. a small group of organisations, for example In Control, working with a group of local authorities demonstrated how self-directed services could work
4. the sense of urgency driven by the looming crisis in social care with an ageing population, growing expectation of quality and demand for more personalised services becoming the norm, with budgets increasingly tightly constrained.

Leadbeater *et al* suggest that these factors have come together and created the conditions for radical innovation. This innovation has the potential to be transformational in that it will, over time, create new workforce structures as traditional services adapt to the demands of individuals, and new, more responsive and flexible services are created that will dramatically change the relationship between users and organisations. Transformative innovations have a long timescale, often decades. This is borne out by the time it has taken since the first demands in the 1980s by disabled people for greater control of their lives and who subsequently established the independent living movement and the principle of direct payments. These early developments laid the foundations for self-directed support and enabled them to buy the assistance and support they needed to live an integrated life in the community, and overcome the social isolation and dependency of life in residential institutions.

How individuals respond to innovation

There is extensive research on how individuals respond to innovation, primarily through the work of Rogers (2003) who identified the stages in the adoption of innovations and devised adopter categories. He described the characteristics of individuals who respond to innovation in terms of their readiness to adopt a new idea, categorising them in terms of 'innovators', 'early adopter' or the 'early' and 'late majority', or 'laggards' who were slowest to adopt. Rogers expresses reservations about using the term 'laggard', which implies it is the individual's fault for being a late adopter, when the system itself may be to blame and that their position may be a realistic one in view of the resources available to them to achieve implementation. Greenhalgh (2005) also cautions that a slow adoption can sometimes be beneficial, for example, when introducing a new drug. Smale (1998) also highlights the risk of pro-innovation bias where individuals are '*open to criticism for their lack of vision when they may actually be right, having perceived the disadvantages of the proposed innovation*'. What this points to is the need for a thorough evaluation of innovations, and processes for deciding which ideas would benefit from explorations and support, as not all ideas for innovation are good ideas (Mulgan & Albury, 2003).

In spite of the above reservations, the value of Rogers' research is in helping those introducing innovations to understand that individuals differ in the willingness to adopt new ideas and that this needs to be understood, and that the position individuals take towards an innovation can be dictated by a wide range of personal, group and organisational factors. It should also be understood that adopting a position towards an innovation is not necessarily fixed in time. Opinions and attitudes can change, as we have seen in the case study of the closure of a children's hospital (see Chapter 6) where some staff strongly opposed to change subsequently became committed enthusiasts following exposure to information and training.

This linear model of adoption has been criticised by Fitzgerald *et al* (2003) as it can underestimate the complexity of health and social care organisations and the inter-professional boundaries that need to be negotiated when innovations are introduced. The authors found this particularly challenging in primary care where professional groups were influenced by different factors, including the robustness of the evidence and the credibility and status of the person providing evidence for important change. This research points to the importance of 'opinion leaders' who can play an important role in facilitating the acceptance of an innovation at a local level (it should also be remembered that opinion leaders can also inhibit innovation!). In their research, Fitzgerald *et al* found that leadership for innovation could be provided by professionals who were seen as experts and whose advice was sought by others. A similar role was held by educators within the postgraduate education system. These findings point to the important role of change agents and innovation champions found across the different research studies into the adoption of innovations.

The innovation–decision process

According to Rogers (2003), when an individual is exposed to a new idea they go through a process which constitutes a series of stages. During this process a series of actions and choices are made in which the individual evaluates the new idea and decides whether to incorporate it into their practice. First, the individual is exposed to the innovation and gains some basic understanding of it (the knowledge stage). This is followed by the formation of an attitude towards it, which can be either positive or negative (the persuasion stage). A decision is then made about whether to adopt or reject it (the decision stage). If the decision is to adopt it, this is followed by individuals putting the innovation into practice (the implementation stage) and finally, there is the confirmation of the decision where the adopter continues to use the innovation. This stage could also lead to the reversal of the decision if the adopter is exposed to information that questions the innovation.

Figure 10.1: Stages of the innovation–decision process

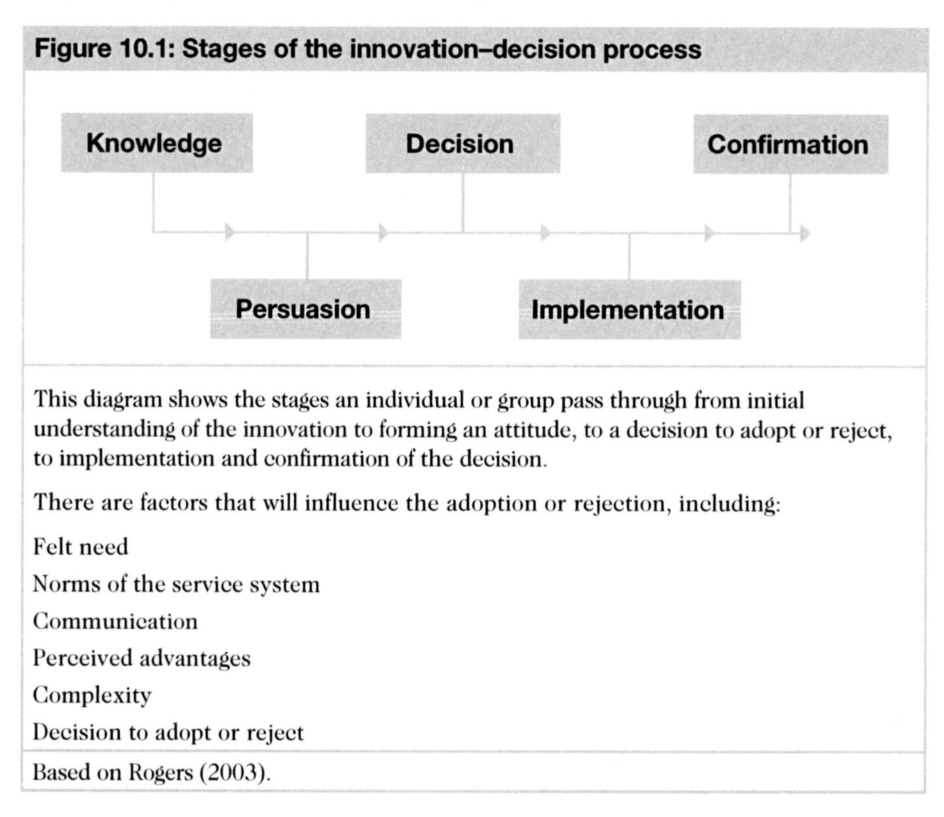

This diagram shows the stages an individual or group pass through from initial understanding of the innovation to forming an attitude, to a decision to adopt or reject, to implementation and confirmation of the decision.

There are factors that will influence the adoption or rejection, including:

Felt need

Norms of the service system

Communication

Perceived advantages

Complexity

Decision to adopt or reject

Based on Rogers (2003).

Another approach to the process of implementing a specific innovation is described by Greenhalgh (2005) as consisting of a checklist which has three phases, each of which identifies those factors that are ideally present.

1. **Before: assessing system readiness**

- Tensions for change where individuals feel that the present state needs improving and are unhappy with the status quo.
- Those who support the innovation outnumber those who oppose it, and are more strategically placed.
- There has been a systematic assessment of how the innovation fits with the organisation's mission and the likely consequences for the organisation.
- There are sufficient resources allocated to the implementation process.
- Systems have been established to monitor the success of the implementation process.

2. **During: drive through change**

- Autonomy to the front line with devolved decision making.
- Leadership from the top and middle is hands on.
- Training and development is provided for the right people at the right time.
- Staff are encouraged to network among themselves to learn and share experience, and link with others outside the organisation.

3. **After: continue to evolve**

- Staff are encouraged to customise the innovation to suit local needs.
- Data is captured on the impact of the innovation and is fed into the quality improvement process.
- Staff are encouraged to join networks of interested users and work on new developments in the area.

In her research on innovation in the NHS, Stocking (1985) concluded that for an innovation to diffuse rapidly it would need to exhibit some or all of the following features:

- the existence of identifiable enthusiasts who originated or discovered the new idea and are keen to disseminate it and have sufficient professional status and time and energy to promote it

- the innovation does not conflict with current national or organisational policies or the established climate of opinion among professionals
- it should have local appeal to those who have the power to promote change
- it should meet the perceived needs of service users and staff and not require a major role or attitude change and be simple to introduce
- it should be easily adaptable to local circumstances
- it should not require additional finance or other resources.

Stocking is not making a value judgment about the quality of the innovations, but simply describing those factors which enable them to 'diffuse rapidly'. If these conditions are met then it is more likely that the innovations will be easier for professionals to adopt. Stocking also notes that her research tends to confirm that within the NHS an innovation in equipment is more readily adopted than changes in organisational behaviour, and suggests that innovations diffuse more rapidly when they are 'add-ons' to existing behaviour and do not require significant role or attitude changes.

What these different models and checklists offer are suggestions for assessing the potential for introducing innovations and identifying where there is potential conflict between the innovation and the individual and organisational factors that can provide a barrier to change. They are also helpful in understanding why innovations are not adopted and lead to a better understanding of the adoption and diffusion process, which in turn leads to more effective innovation processes.

People who can support innovation

The introduction and diffusion of an innovation is dependent on a number of individuals who play a part in promoting and persuading others to adopt the innovation. Without these individuals many innovations would fail. Individuals play different roles and this section will describe those roles and their importance for the innovation process. These roles are described in a wide range of literature on the diffusion of innovations, including Rogers (2003), Stocking (1985) and Smale (1998).

Innovation champions

Innovation champions are individuals who are described as 'early adopters' and spread the message to others (Rogers, 2003). They are seen as crucial for spreading new ideas and methods (Smale, 1998). They are individuals who have a good grasp of the issues surrounding the innovation and are able to convey belief in and enthusiasm about the proposed innovation. They are also likely to have strategic awareness and understanding of relations in the organisation, and are able to enlist the support and involvement of key stakeholders. It is also suggested that innovation champions who can promote and drive innovation are a key factor in success (IDeA, 2005).

Opinion leaders

These are individuals within an organisation or profession who have influence on the practices of others. They are the 'role models' whose behaviour is imitated by others. They are important individuals for those introducing innovations as they lead the opinion of those who will adopt the innovation. Examples would include GPs who become expert in particular conditions and hospital consultants whose views are trusted and who are consulted by GP colleagues (Fitzgerald *et al*, 2003). It should also be remembered that opinion leaders can oppose an innovation and can be a powerful influence against adoption.

Change agents

These play a similar role to those described in Chapter 7. They work through relationships with other people in the organisation as they set out to introduce the innovation, negotiating with others as they analyse the nature of the innovation, and their understanding of context in which the innovation takes place. Their main focus is bringing individuals together to share ideas and to clarify and solve problems. Where managers act as change agents, it is important that they do not use pre-ordained approaches which can discourage critical comment and fail to encourage discussion of alternatives to the managers' preferred solutions (Smale, 1998).

Individuals who legitimise and sponsor innovations

Smale (1998) describes how it can be difficult in some organisations to introduce bottom-up innovations due to senior management attitudes, or where there are a range of prejudices that inhibit innovation. Using more senior colleagues to legitimise or sponsor the initiative can help overcome this resistance. Senior managers can also play an important role in the allocation of resources. Where large financial investment is necessary then senior managers can be important sponsors of innovations.

Generating ideas for innovation

In a discussion of the factors that foster innovation, Mulgan and Albury (2003) list a number of elements that are likely to support innovation. They argue that the public sector cannot depend on government as the main source of ideas – for example, the creation of the NHS in the 1940s – and that many successful innovations were created within public services themselves and that where organisations fail to generate new ideas they are vulnerable to stagnation. The difficulty for public sector organisations is that they can find innovation hard and tend to view new ideas, particularly radical ones, as disruptive and threatening, and often suppress them. They argue that where public sector organisations seek to innovate, they need systematic methods for generating possibilities, as described below.

According to Mulgan and Albury (2003) half of all innovations are initiated by frontline staff and middle managers and it is important that there are processes for ensuring that the views (and complaints) are listened to, and that they are encouraged to continue to provide new ideas. New and younger staff in particular can have important views on what works, does not work and possible improvements, so it is important to listen to them. Therefore, it is important that there are processes for researching and listening to what users and frontline staff say about services. It is recognised that not all staff are innovative and that some actively resist change, but with encouragement and support over time new ideas and possibilities can emerge. They also include service users here, as there is evidence of the way complaints from users about the need to use separate offices and functions have resulted in the innovative development of one-stop shops that integrate services.

Ensuring a diversity of staffing and exploiting difference

Innovation depends on the ability to see things differently. Where organisations have staff from a diversity of backgrounds and ways of thinking and contrasting professional perspectives, it is more likely to promote innovation. These conditions can also create constructive tension and conflict, which is not easy or comfortable, but where innovation can flourish.

Constant scanning of horizons and margins: learning from others

This recognises that individuals and organisations generate ideas for innovation by observing and reflecting on what others are doing and thinking, and by comparing themselves against good practice elsewhere. Innovations on the margins of systems are often the source of change as witnessed in the way that the hospice movement has changed ways of caring for the terminally ill.

Developing the capacity for creative thinking

Creative techniques that help organisations and individuals suspend judgement, rational thought and proven knowledge in order to generate the unexpected is rare in the public sector where there can be cultural barriers to their use in traditional organisations. They are more commonly used in the private sector including the use of techniques such as fiction, role-play, imagining worlds and systematic inventing thinking.

Working backwards from outcome goals

Using methods that work backwards from outcomes – rather than forwards from policies or practices – can often generate a wide range of potential options. For example, in analysing how to achieve more effective services for users, starting with a blank sheet of paper is likely to lead to different conclusions from ones that start with the existing services and their provision.

Creating space

Due to the day-to-day pressures in services there is often little time left to think about or develop innovations that could help reduce the pressures. Pressured work environments leave little time for creativity. Creating time and organisational space where managers and frontline staff can have structured and informal discussion through 'away days' and similar events is critical to creativity.

Breaking the rules

Innovation often occurs where rules are broken and new discoveries can depend on suspending logic. This creates a significant management challenge where rule breaking and the development of dissident cultures are encouraged.

Competition

Within the private sector, competition is a key driver of innovation and although less relevant to the public sector, competitive objectives can help to generate innovative thinking about service delivery.

Organisational conditions that support innovation

In a wide ranging review of the long-term trends in the management and organisation of health care, Ferlie (1999) asks what are the organisational structures and processes that create the conditions for innovation and change. Research has demonstrated that there are severe barriers to change when organisational structures inhibit the generation of ideas and undermine individuals to propose new ways of working that improve services. Large scale public sector organisations are said to be characterised by strong pressures towards inertia, and radical change is both infrequent and risky. These organisations typically have rigid internal boundaries and long hierarchies that block communication and can produce an environment that is inhospitable for the constant innovation that is needed to achieve and sustain success and makes innovation more difficult. Innovation is more likely to occur where there is the presence of flatter organisations, small task groups, and where flexibility and responsiveness are seen as critical factors.

The work of Mintzberg (1983) in categorising organisations suggests reasons why some are more likely to create the conditions for innovation than others. Those organisations he describes as 'machine bureaucracies' have strong hierarchies and central direction, with clear divisions of work and strong line management up to the strategic apex. They are strongly rule bound and organisational cultures stress control. Staff are not expected to develop or promote innovations. They are expected to operate anonymously, preserving confidentiality about their activities and are rarely able to take credit for innovations. The occupation groups are described as semi-professions and strong bureaucratic control systems operate on their work.

Mintzberg contrasts these organisations with professional bureaucracies that have significant numbers of professional staff who exercise considerable autonomy in their work, delivering complex services providing highly skilled and non-routine tasks. These tend to be more innovative organisations as individual professionals contribute to developing new treatments and publicise their achievements through research findings and professional conferences. In order to attract staff to these organisations there is a strong corporate incentive to promote innovation.

Ferlie (1999) argues that knowledge production, rapid learning and effective innovation are emerging as key factors in modern organisations. As we move towards a knowledge-based economy there is increased emphasis on the creation of human capital and the development of sophisticated information systems that enable the rapid transfer of knowledge. These trends point to the crucial role of professionals being more critical to their organisations and needing to be empowered to innovate and maximise public value to the services provided.

Greenhalgh (2005) describes the key characteristics of organisations that are more receptive to innovation. These are likely to have senior managers who are effective in providing vision and leadership, while at middle management level there are good relationships and communication between managers. The management structure is decentralised so that decisions can be taken at a local level and do not have to be passed up the line for approval. Senior staff encourage and facilitate the exchange and sharing of knowledge and ideas, with the creation of a climate where staff are rewarded for taking risks and not punished, even if they sometimes lead to failure. Similarly, staff have the skills and capacity to scan the horizon and identify new ideas. The goals and priorities in relation to projects are clearly articulated and there is sufficient slack in resources so that finance and staffing is available to be allocated to new projects. Where innovations are introduced there is timely feedback on the success of the innovation.

As we saw in Chapter 1, an understanding of the external environment is critical to the future of an organisation. Bryson (2004) sees innovation primarily as a response to real needs and problems, and that the information that drives innovation mostly comes from outside the organisation. Therefore, the more importance that is placed on individuals in an organisation attending to external needs and problems, the greater the likelihood that there will be a climate conducive to innovation, and the easier it will be to justify innovation to others in the organisation. Where an organisation is comfortable with its contact with the outside world and those that bring information from outside the organisation, then they will feel safer to communicate information that demands attention and cannot be ignored. The danger is that organisations can find that they talk primarily to themselves, with all the dangers that they can become 'cut off' or deaf to messages that are telling them that they need to change. Where organisations stay in touch with the external environment that justifies their existence, the greater the likelihood there will be attention given to innovative ideas in order to remain effective.

In their review of organisational change, Iles and Sutherland (2001) examined different models of innovation in order to identify those factors that provide the personal and organisational conditions of innovation. They quote the work of Rogers (2003) which identifies a series of factors that need to be present to increase the likelihood of success.

- **Relative advantage:** this is the degree to which the innovation is perceived to have advantages over the existing technology.
- **Compatibility:** the extent to which the innovation integrates with existing structures, procedures and values.
- **Complexity:** the degree of difficulty involved in learning about and implementing the innovation.
- **Trialability:** the extent to which the innovation can be tried by potential adopters without a major investment in time or resources.
- **Observability:** the degree to which outcomes resulting from the adoption of the innovation are visible.

In addition to the above factors, Greenhalgh (2005) has added the following factors:

- potential for reinvention, if the adopter can customise the innovation to suit a particular context, then they are more likely to adopt it
- minimal risk to the potential adopter (eg. financial or loss of reputation) increases the likelihood of adoption
- nature of knowledge, innovations that come with clear instructions that are easy to follow are more likely to be adopted than those that require practical, uncodifiable tacit knowledge
- technical support where innovations are technology based that come as an augmented product (eg. helpdesk and site maintenance contract) will be more likely to be adopted.

What these factors offer those tasked with introducing the innovation is the opportunity to tailor a change programme so those who have to undertake new practices are exposed to the factors that are more likely to influence their attitudes towards adoption. Innovations are more likely to be rapidly adopted as a result of the presence of a number of these factors, and reduce the risk of resistance to change.

Enablers to innovation

To support innovations in public sector organisations, Borins (2001) provides the following prescriptions.

An innovation culture must be supported from the top: this is seen as critical for innovation to thrive and emerge at all levels. Support can take many forms, including developing organisational priorities to guide innovation, recognition for innovators, creating freedom for experimentation to take place and to protect innovators from organisational constraints.

Increase rewards for innovative individuals and teams: these can take different forms, including financial or recognition-based. It is important to communicate the message that innovators' efforts are valued.

Resources for innovation: this was found to be an obstacle that is difficult to overcome and demonstrates that without adequate resources, innovation will not occur. Borins argues for financial management reforms to create additional funding for innovation within services.

Innovation is everyone's responsibility: organisations that wish to encourage innovation should draw on the ideas of staff at all levels. The point made earlier about frontline staff and middle managers is important to reinforce in view of their crucial role in the generation of innovative ideas.

Scope for experimentation: organisations should reduce the costs to staff when innovations fail as this can promote commitment to experimentation. The creation of 'safe' places such as pilots or zones can facilitate experimentation.

Innovation requires evaluation: innovations need to be robustly evaluated so that learning can take place and lessons drawn from a particular innovation can inform policy and practice.

Involvement of end users: a dialogue with end users of innovations at an early stage can facilitate acceptance and diffusion, and also through the design, development and implementation stages when faults can be identified early and remedied.

Creating the conditions for innovation

Creating, developing and diffusing innovations can be difficult in health and social care organisations due to a range of structural and cultural factors that inhibit experimentation and risk taking, which are essential components of innovation. Organisations need to make innovation a priority which is rooted in their vision and strategy. It is important to ensure that innovation is seen as significant and that there are processes in place which communicate that innovative ideas are welcome. For staff to respond with ideas, leaders need to be seen as people who can be trusted, and who can influence the development of a culture that generates positive ideas for change. They need to ensure that ideas are welcome from all staff and not just those that emanate from the top. Organisations are likely to be more innovative if they signal to their staff that they will be rewarded for developing new initiatives and that attempting to innovate does not risk damage to their careers. Procedures are needed that reassure staff that when they have ideas for improvement they know how to communicate their ideas and where to go to for support, and where decisions are made on how their ideas will be treated. The support of no-blame pilots and no-blame attitudes when pilots fail can encourage innovation.

To move to a more positive position requires managers to support change, take measured risks and test pilots, even though some may fail. If staff are fearful of communicating new ideas it can be a significant barrier to innovation. Managers need to recognise those who attempt to innovate will have both successes and failures. Where ideas fail there needs to be a thorough analysis so that the factors that caused failure can be identified and changes made to future attempts. It is particularly important to avoid a blame culture. Try to identify why an innovation failed and how those who attempt to innovate can be supported. Creating project teams with a change focus could encourage more innovations, as they bring together teams that are multi-skilled and have different specialisms and reduce the focus on individuals when innovations fail.

Most innovation is driven by clear 'levers'. Identifying the levers that need to be pulled to drive innovation is important as these are likely to be related to service performance, finance, clinical, or care processes. Identifying the levers can help focus on what will most likely drive change and accelerate the innovation process (Hayward, 2010). Health and social care organisations also need to take an 'outside-in' perspective, which means viewing the organisation through the eyes of those who use the service and how they perceive it. This can help challenge the assumptions that can become rooted in the way organisations work, and neglect the need for greater awareness of how the organisation is seen by those who use its services.

Lastly, it is important to remember that not all innovations mean progress. There tends to be a pro-innovation bias when new ideas are introduced, and that some innovations turn out to be detrimental to health and well-being. Rogers (2003) gives the example of bottle feeding babies in developing countries where companies promoted the benefits of bottle feeding over breastfeeding. This led to a rapid increase in bottle feeding in some countries, but under the conditions experienced by many families in developing countries, this resulted in life-threatening problems in villages and urban slums. Smale (1998) cautions that when we adopt innovations they have to be good solutions to problems that need solving, without causing more harm than good.

Summary

This chapter has defined what is meant by innovation and how it differs from routine ongoing change in organisations. Innovation can include everyday small scale changes through to transformative changes that create entirely new organisations and ways of working. An important aspect is how individuals respond to innovation, which can be dependent on a wide range of personal and organisational factors, and an understanding of these is crucial for the effective implementation and diffusion of innovation. The key roles played by individuals in the promotion and implementation of innovation are an essential part of the process. How organisations can create the conditions for innovation is crucial as public sector organisations can find it difficult to support innovation due to their mandate and role. Finding ways of enabling innovation is crucial for the future effectiveness of public services.

References

Borins S (2001) *The Challenge of Innovating in Government*. Arlington, Virginia: Pricewaterhouse Coopers Endowment for the Business of Government.

Bryson JM (2004) *Strategic Planning for Public and Nonprofit Organizations: A guide to strengthening and sustaining organizational achievement* (3rd edition). San Francisco: Jossey-Bass Publishers.

Department of Health (2007) *Putting People First: A shared vision and commitment to the transformation of adult social care*. London: DH.

Ferlie E (1999) *No 7 Organisation and Management: Archetype change in the organisation and management of health care?* London: The Nuffield Trust.

Fitzgerald L, Ferlie E & Hawkins C (2003) Innovations in healthcare: how does credible evidence influence professionals? *Health and Social Care in the Community* **11** (3) 219–228.

GB Equal Support Unit (2006) *Measuring and sustaining innovation: A guide for development partnerships* [online]. Birmingham: GB Equal Support Unit. Available at: www.equal.ecotec.co.uk (accessed September 2010)

Greenhalgh T (2005) *Strategic Workshop: How to spread good ideas* (resource pack). London: University College London and National Prescribing Centre.

Halrorsen T, Hauknes J, Miles I & Roste R (2005) *On the Difference Between Public and Private Sector Innovation*. Public report no. 9D Oslo. NIFU STEP.

Hayward S (2010) How to create a climate for innovation *People Management*, 11th February.

IDeA (2005) *Innovation in Public Services* [online]. Available at: http://www.idea.gov.uk/idk/aio/1118552 (accessed June 2010).

Iles V & Sutherland K (2001) *Organisational Change: A review for health care managers, professionals and researchers*. London: London School of Hygiene and Tropical Medicine.

Johnson K & Williams I (2007) *Managing Uncertainty and Change in Social Work and Social Care*. Lyme Regis: Russell House Publishing.

Leadbeater C, Bartlett J & Gallagher N (2008) *Making it Personal*. London: Demos. Available at: www.demos.co.uk/publications/makingitpersonal (accessed September 2010)

Mintzberg H (1983) *Structures in Five*. New York: Prentice Hall.

Mulgan G & Albury D (2003) *Innovation in the Public Sector*. London: Prime Minister's Strategy Unit, Cabinet Office.

Rogers EM (2003) *Diffusion of Innovations* (5th edition). London: Collier Macmillan Publishers.

Smale G (1998) *Managing Change Through Innovation*. London: The Stationery Office.

Stocking B (1985) *Initiative and Inertia: Case studies in the NHS*. London: The Nuttfield Provincial Hospitals Trust.

Chapter 11

Drawing the strands together

Summary of the chapters

A wide range of topics have been examined in this book and the starting point was the importance of understanding what drives change and the actions that managers need to take to identify the source and range of forces acting on their organisation.

Chapter 1 warns that a constant awareness of changes, particularly in the external environment, is essential if organisations are to respond in a timely way. Ignorance of the external environment of the organisation and an unwillingness to take hard decisions inevitably lead to poor performance and ultimately, decline.

Chapter 2 is concerned with the different forms of change, whether they are strategic or operational. Strategic change is large scale and long-term, whereas operational change is concerned with continual improvements and adjustments to services. Whatever form change takes, all organisations are susceptible to strategic drift if they fail to understand their external environment and the forces for change. The extent to which organisations are in tune with their environment will, to a great extent, influence the degree of change necessary for survival.

Chapter 3 examined the concept of the context in which organisations operate. This chapter draws on a number of significant research studies of health care organisations that have identified the contextual features, and the conditions that can create receptive or non-receptive environments for change. This chapter is useful in alerting managers to some of the crucial factors that influence the potential success of change strategies based on evidence from a wide range of research locations.

Chapter 4 focuses on organisational culture and its importance in the management of change. We have seen in this chapter that culture is a complex concept to capture, but one that managers neglect at their peril when it comes to implementing change. Culture change can be difficult to manage as it can be so deeply embedded in the behaviours and actions of individuals, whether senior managers or staff at the front line. The notion of the paradigm and the cultural web is important here as it provides managers with a way of understanding why change can be difficult to achieve in the face of forces that are often hard to identify without the aid of cultural mapping.

Chapter 5 explored leadership and its importance in the management of change. All successful change strategies have at the core a determined and sustained leadership by a wide range of individuals, including senior managers, frontline managers, professionals and change champions. This chapter has argued that leadership in change is less about single charismatic individuals, but a coalition of committed individuals who work effectively together. In this way leadership is found at many levels in the organisation and as a result more likely to ensure successful change.

Chapter 6 helps us understand how individuals may respond to change. In any change process the most important factor is the people who will need to make change to work in practice. How they react to change will be largely dependent on their relationship with their organisation, and particularly those leading and implementing change. Skilfully managing the change process means recognising the contribution of individuals and providing support and training as they are asked to work in new ways.

Chapter 7 is concerned with the management of the change process, including the level of participation in planning change and timescales and responsibilities. Complex change means a range of people are involved including change agents and external consultants. How implementation is planned, and techniques that can be used to assess the forces surrounding change is crucial to success. The resources needed to support change and the different styles of managing change are also considered. Lastly, suggestions are made for the evaluation of change, which is often neglected, with its lessons for future change initiatives lost without this vital stage.

Chapter 8 considers the role of stakeholders and the importance in understanding the way that they can influence the outcome of change due to their power and influence. We have seen that stakeholders can be both internal and external to the organisation, but it is the external stakeholders who can surprise managers by their resistance to change and their potential to generate opposition to proposals, particularly if their views are ignored or taken for granted. Understanding the position of different stakeholders and their views in relation to a change proposal should be central to the management of change. Here the concept of stakeholder mapping offers a means of identifying the power and influence of stakeholders in relation to a particular change proposal.

Chapter 9 explored change in inter-professional practice and how organisations are being transformed to ensure more effective service delivery. Emphasis is placed on the leadership of inter-professional teams and the need for professionals to explore new ways of working which encompass practices, roles and team membership. A series of examples of changes in service delivery are used to illustrate some of the complexities of inter-professional practice. Lastly, this chapter suggests actions that leaders can consider when leading in inter-professional contexts.

Chapter 10 explored innovation and how it differs from routine change. Innovations have the potential to improve practice, but also to radically change the way services are delivered or even create new service forms. The introduction and diffusion of innovations can be dependent on a wide range of personal and organisational factors that need to be considered when new ideas are being promoted. The importance of key opinion leaders and their support for innovation is an essential part of the process of diffusion.

Taken together these 10 chapters encompass some of the main elements in the management of change. Each stage of the change process is considered, drawing on research and best practice. As health and social care services face up to a future where large scale change is planned, alongside severe financial cutbacks, the importance of understanding the change process from initial analysis through implementation to evaluation, using well established and tested approaches, is even more essential. This book provides you with the ideas and techniques that you can use when managing change that can significantly increase the likelihood of successful implementation, based on the fundamental values of respect for those using services and the staff who support them.

Further resources

Further resources

The following suggestions for further reading provide useful information and ideas on change management.

Books

Brown J (1996) *Chance Favours the Prepared Mind*. London: The Stationery Office.

This explores the introduction of new service developments and innovations in social work, describing the process from foundation to implementation.

Bryson JM (2004) *Strategic Planning for Public and Nonprofit Organizations: A guide to strengthening and sustaining organizational achievement* (3rd edition). San Francisco: Jossey-Bass.

An American book, aimed primarily at the third sector, providing a detailed guide to strategic planning and change, with a wide range of tools and techniques explained to enable the manager to implement change successfully.

Gilbert P (2005) *Leadership: Being effective and remaining human*. Lyme Regis: Russell House Publishing.

This book has much to say about the importance of leadership and its role in improving and changing services.

Johnson G, Scholes K & Whittington R (2008) *Exploring Corporate Strategy* (8th edition). Harlow: Pearson Education.

This explores a wide range of strategic issues, linking theory and practice with numerous case examples. It mainly focuses on the business sector but has much that is important about the development and implementation of strategy for managers in the public sector.

Smale G (1998) *Managing Change through Innovation*. London: The Stationery Office.

An invaluable guide to the complexities of introducing change in social care services. It offers a detailed framework, taking the reader through each stage of the change process.

Upton T & Brooks B (1995) *Managing Change in the NHS*. Buckingham: Open University Press.

A short practical handbook that is full of ideas about how to manage the change process with numerous case examples and checklists.

Web documents

IDeA (2005) *Innovation in Public Services* (literature review). Available at: www.idea.gov.uk

This reviews what is known about innovation in public services, drawing on a wide range of sources with short case examples of innovation.

Fitzgerald L (2006) *Making Change Happen in the NHS: Clinical and management tasks* (briefing paper 21). Available at: www.sdo.nihr.ac.uk/files/adhoc/21-briefing-paper.pdf

A report of the research led by Fitzgerald and colleagues that examined the ways that managers from clinical and non-clinical backgrounds carried out their roles in the process of service improvements.

Greenhalgh T, Robert G, Bate P, Macfarlane F, Kyriakidou O & Peacock R (2004) *Spreading and Sustaining Innovations in Health Service Delivery and Organisation* (briefing paper 38). Available at: www.sdo.nihr.ac.uk/files/adhoc/38-briefing-paper.pdf

A systematic literature review by Greenhalgh and colleagues on how innovations spread and what makes successful innovation more likely.

Iles V & Sutherland K (2001) *Organisational Change: A review for health care managers, professionals and researchers*. NHS Service Delivery and Organisation R&D Programme. Available at: www.sdo.nihr.ac.uk

This reviews the research literature on the management of change with theories, tools, models and approaches evaluated.

Iles V & Cranfield S (2004) *Developing Change Management Skills: A resource for health care professionals and managers*. NHS Service Delivery and Organisation R&D Programme. Available at: www.sdo.nihr. ac.uk

A companion document to the above text with emphasis on the practical application of the tools and techniques described with extensive case studies of change management.

Mulgan G & Albury D (2003) *Innovation in the Public Sector*. Available at: www. cabinetoffice.gov.uk

A discussion paper on the conditions necessary for successful innovation in public services.

Websites

Department of Health's extensive website has policy, research, practice guidance and general information on all aspects of health and social care.

Available at: www.dh.gov.uk

Improvement and Development Agency (IDeA) works with local authorities and their partners supporting improvement and innovation and the development of good practice. There is a wide range of change projects on their website.

Available at: www.idea.gov.uk

NHS Institute for Innovation and Improvement supports the NHS in transforming health care through developing and spreading new ways of working, new technology and leadership developments.

Available at: www.institute.nhs.uk

NHS Service Delivery and Organisation (SDO) commissions independent research that supports the organisation and delivery of health care and the work of partner organisations such as local authorities. Its briefing papers are an excellent source of information on current research in health care.

Available at: www.sdo.nihr.ac.uk

Social Care Institute of Excellence (SCIE) identifies and spreads knowledge about good practice to the social care workforce to support the delivery of transformed and personal social care services.

Available at: www.scie.org.uk